How to s

HOME RECORDING

How to set up a
HOME RECORDING
STUDIO

David Mellor

PC Publishing

PC Publishing
Export House
130 Vale Road
Kent TN9 1SP
UK

Tel 01732 770893
Fax 01732 770268
e-mail pcp@cix.compulink.co.uk

First published 1990
Reprinted 1992
Second edition 1996

© David Mellor

ISBN 1 870775 43 0

British Library Cataloguing in Publication Data

A catalogue record for this book is available from the British Library

Printed and bound in Great Britain by Bell and Bain, Glasgow

Preface

There is no better hobby than making music, and there is no more satisfying business to get into. Many of us enjoy making music so much that we want to make it into a career. And it isn't just a vague dream — it really is something that is achievable. Many pretty ordinary people are making money out of music right now, even if it isn't their main source of income. They are enjoying what they are doing, and they are doing it to a professional standard. At the heart of modern music making is the studio, whatever type of studio it may be. Call it a home studio or a project studio, a well designed studio facility will enable you to create a demo tape that will start you off on your recording career, or with a bit of luck you might find yourself composing and recording music for television and film. Even if you just do it for your own pleasure and amusement, as I said there is no better hobby.

Setting up a home or project recording studio can be a tricky business, and it's easy to spend a lot money and waste a lot of effort. There is more to setting up a studio than just buying the equipment. It's how the equipment is set up and the surroundings that are important. Your studio should be an environment in which you can feel comfortable and creative, in which you can sit down and start work without any preparation or messing about with the equipment. You just go in there and start making music. And when your tape is finished, it is perfectly possible that your recording might be as good as anything a full time professional engineer could have produced in a commercial studio.

I have had a recording studio at home for nearly 15 years now, since the days when people thought you had to hire a 'proper' recording studio to do anything worthwhile. I, amongst others, have proved the doubters wrong and recordings I have made at home have appeared on vinyl, CD, radio, television, commercials and films all the way from the United States to Japan and Australia. And I'm not doing anything you couldn't do. It will take quite a bit of hard work to set up the studio and gain sufficient experience in using it, but musical success can be within your grasp if you want it badly enough.

In a way I envy you, because you are at the start of a great adventure, and the equipment that is available now for people just starting out is much better than it used to be. But manufacturers will often only tell you about the easy options. Buying the equipment is as easy as saving up the money, but putting it all together properly needs know how. The know how is in this book, it brings together all the experience I have gained in professional audio, and it tells you how professional studios are put together in a way that you can copy at home. Sometimes, where the difficulties really are too great, you will have to compromise a little, but that won't stop you having a great studio and making great recordings. Take care to read everything and understand as much as you can before you start work. As the saying goes, a journey of a thousand miles starts with a single step, so turn the page and we'll begin...

Contents

1

Types of home studio

Studios fall into three basic categories, home studios, project studios and commercial studios. It's pretty obvious what a home studio is. Many people working in the music industry, and even the TV and film industries, have their own studios at home. They put them in the spare room, the garage, the basement, an outhouse – even in a corner of a bedroom sometimes. And there is no reason why a home studio shouldn't produce recordings that challenge top commercial facilities. Obviously in a top commercial studio, helpful staff will make it easier for you to do your best work, the equipment and acoustics will be first class, and you will probably be working with top musicians too – there may even be a restaurant and bar! Of course the top studio is always going to be that little bit better – but it really is just a little bit. You can do professional work in a bedroom. Sometimes simplicity sells, and you don't always need a 24-track studio to make a song demo or a soundtrack for a documentary.

There really isn't any difference between a home studio and a so-called project studio. A home studio is a project studio that you have at home, so that's easily dealt with. So what's the difference between a project studio and a commercial studio? Simply, a commercial studio is available to allcomers at an hourly or daily rate. Make a booking, do your stuff in the studio, pay the invoice and collect the tape. A project studio is something owned by one person, or maybe a partnership, where the owner or owners work on their own projects. The owner may be a musician working on a CD, or a composer working on a TV soundtrack. Commercial bookings are not welcome in a project studio because:

(a) they are taking up studio time that the owner would probably rather use, and
(b) once you start hiring your studio out as a facility you become involved in many more health and safety regulations and your insurance premiums will probably go through the roof.

What people do in their project studios is of course literally their own business! But I have identified at least five distinct categories of project studio. Let's take a look at what you can achieve, if you have a mind to...

DJ studio

If you are not a DJ, please don't start that old 'DJs are not musicians' routine. That one has been around since the electric guitar was first invented, and it's as wrong to distance yourself from new technical and musical developments as it has ever been. DJs are people who take musical material from whatever sources they need and put sounds together in ways that conventional musicians haven't even dreamed of yet. OK, so there are plenty of people who call themselves DJs who just segue one record into another, which you might not call creative in the normal sense of the word, but you have to look at the kind of money some of them earn for even just a couple of hours work!

Many DJs obviously do their work live, but there is an increasing momentum towards having a studio where mixing can be done at leisure, and a day's creativity can be distilled into one mix that can be taken to the club and played as an exclusive that no other DJ has. A vocalist can be brought in and a totally new song created without anyone ever playing an instrument in the conventional way. The creators of the original sampled material will, if everyone plays fair, be credited and financially rewarded.

Since the object here is to create new music principally by putting existing recorded sounds together in a different way, we need the best means possible of accessing those sounds. Although there is a wide variety of material available on CD, it still doesn't seem to be taking over from vinyl records yet, and shows no sign of ever doing so. That's probably because the whole art of DJing is 'hands on', and hands on is the one thing CDs will never be. The centrepiece of the DJ studio will always be the twin decks and mixer. Note the terminology – 'decks' are what other sound engineering types call turntables (old hands at the BBC still call them 'grams'!). And I have never heard a DJ talk about a 'mixing console', it's always just a mixer. I tend to use the term 'mixing console' because in a recording studio sometimes 'mixer' can be taken to mean the person that is doing the mixing, not the equipment.

If you are a DJ, then you already know about the Technics SL1200 and SL1210 decks. These are the classic models and I suspect they never will be superseded – they have become part of the art form. But exactly why are they so great? The main reason is that the Technics SL1200 and SL1210 both have an extremely powerful direct drive motor. 'Direct drive' means that the turntable itself is part of the motor, and doesn't need to be driven by a belt or idler wheel. Having such a powerful motor means that the turntable can bring the record from a standing start up to the correct speed almost instantaneously. So when the DJ holds back the record on the slip mat, the turntable is still turning at the correct speed despite the friction, and the record is ready to go at the flick of a finger. The SLs come with pickup arm already fitted but you have a choice of cartridge. The prime requirement here is that the cartridge must be tough enough to stand plenty of abuse. Back cueing (turning the record backwards by hand) is a killer for any normal cartridge but those that are specially designed for the purpose can stand it. Stanton is a very well respected make, and Shure too have suitable cartridges in their range. As with any musical activity, it isn't a bad idea to see what the professionals are currently using because if it works for them, it can work for you too, and you might save yourself a lot of effort barking up the wrong tree.

A DJ mixer is distinctly different to any other type of mixing console. It is split into two sets of inputs with a crossfader in between. Obviously the idea is to fade between two records, but the crossfader will fade between any pair of inputs on opposite sides of the mixer. There are all sorts of mixers at all levels of quality. The thing you want to avoid most is a noisy crossfader so ask the supplier whether the cross fader can easily be replaced when necessary. On a high quality mixer, the crossfader may do its job perfectly well for years.

Some DJ mixers have rudimentary samplers built in. But for studio rather than live use it's better to have a proper sampler. Consider ease of use. Some samplers are designed specifically to sample notes from instruments and allocate them to keys on a MIDI keyboard. They don't make it as easy as a DJ would like it to be simply to snatch a piece of vocal or sample a couple of seconds from a record. Products will evolve, but look for ease of use from the DJ's point of view rather than the keyboard player's. The ability to 'scratch' a sample is never found on samplers sold to keyboard players. Speaking of keyboards, you will almost certainly need a MIDI keyboard to get the most from your samples. Look for a 'master' or 'mother' keyboard that doesn't produce any sounds of its own. They can be much cheaper than complete synthesisers.

If you are going to record vocals yourself, you will need a good microphone. I will mention mics, and also recorders, power amplifiers and speakers in detail shortly for the other types of home and project studio.

Figure 1.1 Soundcraft D-MIX 1000 – a high quality DJ mixer

MIDI studio

The object of the MIDI studio is to use MIDI controlled synthesisers, synth modules and samplers as 'live' sound sources, without doing any recording of audio signals until the final mixing stage. There are two advantages in creating music in this way: the first is that MIDI systems don't have any rewind time and you can get to any part of your composition instantly. Secondly, it is possible to change any part of the composition at any later date. This can be very important if you are recording music for a video sound track and the director suddenly calls and tells you that thirty seconds have been cut out of a scene. One of the disadvantages of MIDI systems is that the musical notes and sounds are held in memory and on disk as computer data, and computer data has a nasty habit of corrupting, or simply not coming back the way you expect the day after you created it. The problem is normally human rather than computer error, but it is terribly frustrating to lose something which you have been working on long and hard.

A good starting point for a MIDI studio is a synthesiser, a sampler and a sequencer. The three S's if you like. With a sampler, you have access to a vast range of sounds, particularly if you can connect a CD-ROM drive and access the growing library of CD-ROM sounds that are now available (at a price!). The advantage of a synthesiser is that it is usually easier to fine tune a sound from not-quite-right to absolutely spot on. The combination of a synth and a sampler is very powerful. Since in a pure MIDI studio you have no means of storing sounds on multitrack tape, your equipment should be able to produce several different sounds at the same time. For this you need multi-timbral equipment. Samplers can have four or eight outputs, sometimes more, each of which can produce a completely different sound. Synths are sometimes internally multi-timbral, but several sounds are often constrained to come out of a single stereo output, which does restrict versatility. The sequencer will be in control of the whole system. Most people use computer sequencers these days, although there are still excellent stand-alone sequencers available which have certain advantages. Figure 1.2 shows how to connect the MIDI cables in a small system.

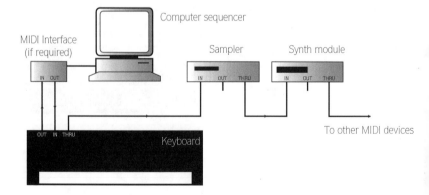

Figure 1.2 Connecting a simple MIDI sequencer system (audio connections not shown)

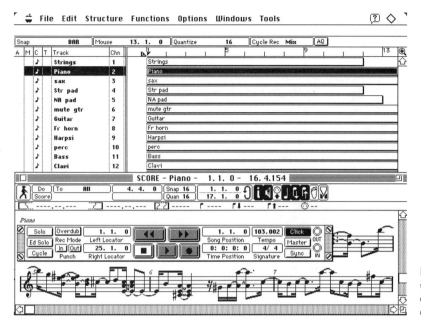

Figure 1.3 Cubase Score
sequencing software running
on an Apple Macintosh
computer

The mixing console you use in a MIDI system need not be as complex as one that is used for multitrack recording. In fact a PA mixer can offer all the facilities you need: plenty of channels, a stereo output, EQ and auxiliary sends. Look for a separate monitor output with a monitor volume control so that you can adjust the level in your speakers independent of the level of the stereo mix going to tape. Not all PA mixing consoles have these features.

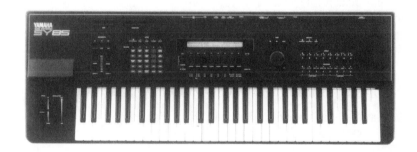

Figure 1.4 Don't compromise
on the keyboard. One
professional quality synth
may be all you need

For mastering, undoubtedly you will aspire to a DAT recorder. Digital Audio Tape is now the professional standard and there are few reasons to use anything else. If you can't afford DAT yet, then you will have to make do with cassette for the moment, but bear in mind that you will never achieve professional results this way. Even the best cassette decks don't have good enough sound quality, particularly when it comes to making copies of your masters. Use a cassette deck for mastering only while you are practising your skills. Reel to reel tape however is still a very viable option and has the advantage that the tape is easy to edit with simple equipment and materials. I still have a reel to reel stereo recorder as well as a DAT and I won't be getting rid of it until it wears out sometime in the very distant future. I no longer need it for editing because I have digital editing equipment, but I still love that old analogue sound!

To hear what you are creating with your MIDI equipment, you need monitoring – a stereo power amplifier and speakers. Hifi equipment is OK to start off with, but once again you should be using the same equipment as the pros use. The power amplifier should be just that with two inputs, two outputs and a mains switch – no other controls apart from volume controls maybe, and definitely no tone controls! 'Near field' monitor speakers are available at a reasonable price which are exactly the same models as you will find in the top professional studios. I won't name names since fashions in monitoring will undoubtedly change, but look out for the near field monitors perched on top of the mixing console in photos of pro studios, and match them up to what you see in adverts. You can't go wrong!

Where you can go wrong however is when you want to have 'main' monitors as well as near fields. Near field monitors are small and therefore don't produce much bass. Main monitors are larger and can produce the bass, but it's not always as accurate as it should be. You may end up making bad judgments about how much bass you put on your recording because of deficiencies in the speakers. I would go for top of the range hifi speakers for main monitors because they are more accurate than speakers that are probably more suitable for PA because of their greater efficiency and sheer sound output.

I use B&W 801 main monitors on the grounds that, if they are good enough for Abbey Road, they are good enough for me – and they are good! Although I do stress that you should take note of what professionals use, because they have learnt their trade and you are learning yours, in the end decisions on sound quality are down to your own ears. Sooner or later you are going to have to trust them.

Recording studio

Well, after all, this book is all about how to set up a home recording studio! By 'recording studio' it is generally understood that you can bring in any combination of musicians with any combination of instruments, up to the physical capacity of the room, playing any style of music, and make a successful recording. To do this you must have a multitrack tape recorder, either analogue or digital. You may even have a multitrack hard disk recorder and it will achieve the same ends. Modular digital multitracks (sometimes called MDMs) are popular since you can start off with one and add more, which will synchronise quite easily, as finances permit. The recording studio may incorporate MIDI equipment, but it's a bigger, all-encompassing concept than the MIDI studio.

For such an all-encompassing concept, a more complex mixing console

is necessary. All recording consoles have a monitoring section, which is in effect a mixer within a mixer. The monitoring section allows you to listen to, and make a temporary mix of, the sounds that you have already recorded to tape as you continue to add overdubs. Although it may be possible to use a cheaper PA console and make perfectly adequate recordings, I wouldn't advise it unless you really know what you are doing. Amazingly enough, even the lowest cost consoles from the reputable manufacturers offer excellent sound quality. If you can afford to pay more, then you will get extra channels and extra facilities, and digital recording consoles are now available at the top end of the project studio price bracket which have features that were once the domain of the highest cost studio facilities only. Don't forget that any professional mixing console should be able to provide phantom power to capacitor microphones.

If you want to have a truly versatile recording studio, then you will need a selection of microphones. Don't skimp on mics – if you don't capture a good sound in the first place, there is no equaliser or effects unit on Earth that will help you. A good mic is particularly important for vocals. I would recommend a large diaphragm capacitor microphone from one of the major manufacturers. These can be extraordinarily expensive, but there are a number of cheaper alternatives coming onto the market which are worth checking out. The advantage of a large diaphragm capacitor microphone is that it gives a very crisp clear sound and vocals really stand out in the mix. Small diaphragm capacitor microphones can be more accurate, but accuracy isn't always that necessary. Since small diaphragm capacitor microphones are less expensive than the larger variety, you can aspire to owning several eventually. Dynamic microphones are valuable too since classic models can be bought for just over £100. The Shure catalogue is the one to look into. Once upon a time I might have said that you shouldn't even bother looking at anything less expensive, but I have a feeling that manufacturers are going to take the budget end of the market a lot more seriously in future. But you'll still need at least one high class mic for vocals, if you do buy inexpensive mics, make sure that they

TIP

You may be led to believe that because digital recording is very popular at the moment that it is the only way to record. If that was so, why would just about every top commercial studio be fully kitted out with analogue multitrack recorders, with digital available as an extra? Two inch 24-track recorders will be used until they wear out, and don't forget that there are plenty of budget multitrack analogue recorders available on the secondhand market.

Figure 1.5 The AKG C3000 is a large diaphragm capacitor mic at a reasonable cost

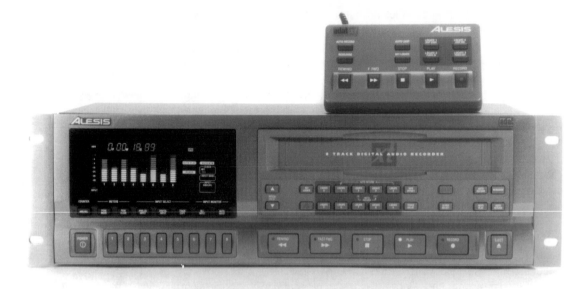

Figure 1.6 The Alesis ADAT XT 8-track modular digital multitrack recorder and remote control

have a balanced output or you may damage them with phantom power – there'll be more on balancing later.

In a recording studio, your musicians will need to be able to hear themselves clearly, and also hear what they has already been recorded on the tape. For this you need a headphone amplifier and several pairs of headphones. Some studios just use an ordinary power amplifier, but you do have to take certain precautions to avoid blowing the headphones. A proper headphone amplifier with sockets for four or more pairs of headphones is best.

Figure 1.7 The Mackie 8 Bus mixing console is popular with professional project studios

Pre-production studio

A pre-production studio is one where the owner starts off a project on his or her own basic equipment with the specific intention of taking it to a commercial studio to finish. Working like this has tremendous cost advantages because you don't have to pay an expensive hourly rate until you need to. And if you start work on a song and find that it's not really going anywhere, at least you have only wasted time. Basically, all a pre-production studio need consist of is some MIDI instruments and a sequencer, with amp and speakers for monitoring obviously. Don't acquire more MIDI equipment than you think you'll take to the commercial studio however otherwise you'll end up being a full-blown home recording studio owner when you probably don't want to be.

The problem with doing pre-production in this way is that you have to take the whole MIDI system to the studio to transfer the basic tracks to tape. You might be better off having a multitrack recorder at home onto which you can record the basic tracks, together with timecode, and just take the recorder and tape to the commercial studio with you. A digital multitrack will fit nicely into the boot of a car. As an extension of this philosophy, it is also quite possible to do pre-production at home, do some recording in a commercial studio, copy the tracks to digital multitrack and then do some more work back at home. You will need a bit of technical knowledge, and you will have to choose a helpful studio, but this way you really do get the best of both the project and commercial studio worlds.

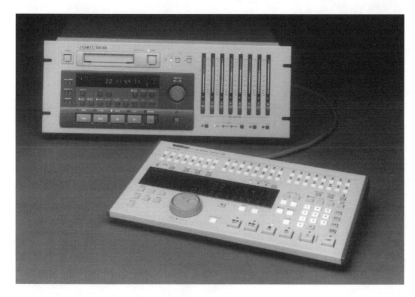

Figure 1.8 The Tascam DA-88 8-track modular digital multitrack recorder and remote control

Connecting the equipment

Many readers will already have a pretty good idea of how to connect the equipment. In case you don't already, here is a quick guide on how to hook up the equipment in a typical multitrack recording studio:

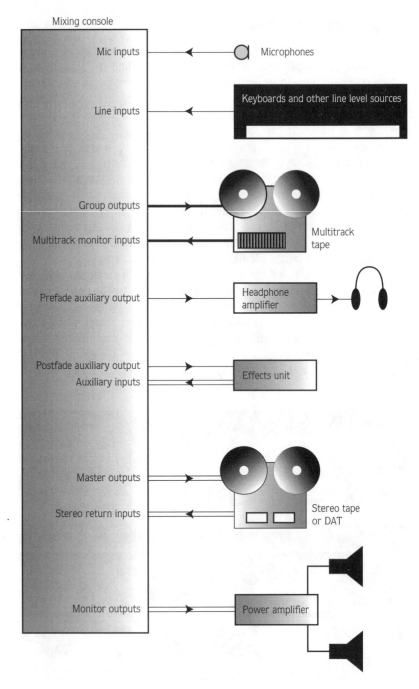

Figure 1.9 Mixing console connections in a recording studio

Microphones are connected to the microphone inputs of the mixing console. Mics have a very low output voltage, which makes them different to just about all other types of sound equipment so they need a special input. Anything else will be connected to the mixing console's line inputs. Electric guitars without internal preamps are a special case because they can only provide a very low output current. Usually it's best to amplify them in the normal way and use a microphone on the speaker cabinet.

The mixing console will have 'group' outputs or sometimes special multitrack outputs which go to the inputs of the multitrack tape recorder. The outputs of the multitrack tape recorder will be connected to multitrack monitor inputs on the mixing console. These go under a variety of names, so check the console's manual.

The mix or master output of the console is the final stereo output which is connected to your stereo recorder, cassette, DAT or reel-to-reel. The console will have two '2T return' or 'stereo return' (always different names!) inputs to which you should connect the outputs of your stereo recorder. There will be a switch on the console which allows you to listen to either the console's master output or playback from the stereo machine. The monitor outputs of the mixing console are connected to a stereo power amplifier, which obviously is then connected to the speakers.

So that the musician or musicians that you are recording can hear themselves and tracks that have already been recorded you should connect a prefade auxiliary output from the console (consult the manual if you are unsure about what a prefade auxiliary is) to a headphone amplifier that will drive as many pairs of headphones as you need.

To add reverb to your mix, connect a postfade auxiliary output from the console to the input of an effects unit. The effects unit will have two outputs which should be connected to the auxiliary inputs (sometimes called auxiliary returns) of the console. Compressors and noise gates are connected to the console when they are needed via channel or group insert point send and return connections.

Of course, all of these connections should really be made via a patchbay, as explained in Chapter 7, but this will at least get you started.

Audio for video

'Audio for video' is a term that covers a wide range of activities including music, dialogue and sound effects. I'll assume that you are primarily interested in recording music to picture. As well as all the components of the recording studio, you will also need a video machine (it doesn't have to be able to record) and a synchroniser. You can record music to picture with a MIDI setup, in which case the requirements for the synchroniser are somewhat less stringent.

You can easily use a domestic VHS for recording music to picture. All you have to do is get the production company to send you a cassette of the programme with LTC (longitudinal timecode – usually just called timecode) on the audio track and preferably also burnt in timecode, where the timecode numbers appear on the screen. If you have a digital multitrack, then you will be able to buy an accessory card or unit which will allow it to synchronise to timecode in a basic way. The only problem you will have is that when you wind the video back to the start of the programme, the multitrack will stay firmly in stop mode until the video starts playing and timecode is issued once more. Only then does it start to rewind. This is a nuisance, but it doesn't stop you working. The next step is to buy a professional grade video and slightly more sophisticated synchroniser that will accept transport commands so that as soon as you start rewinding the video, the tape will rewind too. This method of operation is much quicker, but you'll pay for it.

If you are ambitious and intend synchronising dialogue and sound effects to picture, then you need a hard disk recorder that is suited to the task (some are not). Briefly, you should look at computer based hard disk recording systems where you can see the audio split up into segments on the screen. If the system offers this, and can synchronise successfully to SMPTE/EBU timecode or MTC (MIDI timecode) then it is worth your while getting a thorough demonstration and test drive.

Synchronisation

As you will realise by now, if you want to synchronise a MIDI sequencer with multitrack tape, or if you want to synchronise a multitrack to video, then you need a synchroniser in your system. Synchronisation revolves around SMPTE/EBU timecode which is in essence a numerical identification of every frame on the video in hours:minutes:seconds:frames form. Timecode is recorded either as an audio signal on one track of the multitrack or on an audio track of the video. A digital multitrack can, with the right accessory, record timecode onto a data area of the tape so you don't lose an audio track. In a simple system, the master machine (the multitrack or video) will send timecode to the synchroniser which will control the slave machine in such a way that it always records or plays in sync with the master. The slave could be a MIDI system or a multitrack recorder.

Since SMPTE/EBU timecode has all the appearances of being an audio signal, it is tempting to treat it as an audio signal and allow it to enter areas that should belong only to real audio – the mixing console for instance. This isn't a good idea since timecode sounds awful and easily leaks into audio signal paths where you would rather it didn't. The answer is to run timecode directly from the generator to the multitrack (in your project studio you should never need to stripe timecode onto a video, a procedure which requires a more expensive timecode generator, with a video input, to do properly), and take the timecode output from the multitrack or video directly to the synchroniser. The problem you will have is that when you are striping timecode onto the multitrack tape you will need to control the level, yet many timecode generators have no output level control! The answer is either temporarily go through the mixer to stripe timecode then disconnect the generator, or buy a generator with an output level control. I know which solution I prefer. Since this book is about setting up a studio, you will have to look elsewhere to see how synchroniser systems work because they can get quite complicated, but Figure 1.10 shows a couple of simple systems so that at least you know how they should be connected.

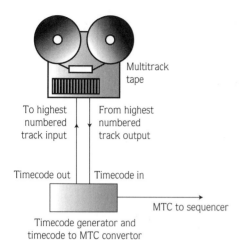

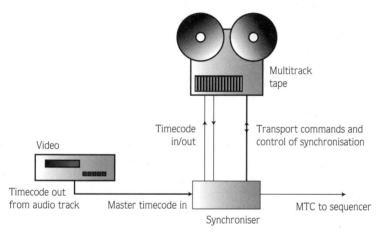

Figure 1.10 Synchronising a MIDI system to multitrack tape

Synchronising multitrack tape and a MIDI system to video

One room or two?

Commercial studios almost always have two rooms, plus office, kitchen, recreation areas etc. One room is the studio where the musicians perform and the other is the control room which houses all the equipment apart from the microphones. Two rooms are necessary because the engineer must be able to judge the sound from the speakers in isolation from the natural acoustic sound of the instruments or vocals. Also, if the microphones could pick up sound from the speakers, then that sound would be recorded on the tape too, and in the worst case feedback could occur. Usually, the two rooms are visually connected via a double or triple glazed window, and access from one room to the other will often be via two doors enclosing a small lobby.

By all means, the home or project studio should imitate this arrangement since it really is the best way of working. But since two rooms are rarely available, compromise is necessary. The best solution is to run permanent lines to another part of the building that is suitable for use as a studio. Remember that you need lines for headphones as well as as many mics as you think you will need. The connectors should be mounted on a panel or metal box so that they are easily available for use.

2

Soundproofing

The subject of soundproofing is so problematical that it will probably make you wish you had taken up a nice quiet hobby like photography! The biggest problem is that one person's music is another person's noise. Any music that leaks out of your studio into your neighbour's house or flat is going to be regarded, to a significant extent, as an annoyance. Particularly so because recording involves going over the same piece of music again and again. You will need either to come to an arrangement with your neighbours about how much noise you will make and at what times you will make it, or apply soundproofing treatment to your recording room. The alternatives could be a lawsuit and possible confiscation of your equipment!

The first thing to note about soundproofing is that it is impossible! There is no such thing as a completely soundproof room. It is a matter of degree. You might reduce the amount of sound leakage by 20 decibels, or if you can afford it by perhaps as much as 45dB or more. The more sound insulation you require, the more it is going to cost, and it can get expensive. Good soundproofing requires three things: mass, decoupling and attention to detail.

Upholstery foam and mineral wool are great for acoustic treatment but they are virtually useless for soundproofing because they are not very massive and they are full of holes. Sound isn't frightened of anything but sheer mass and the holes are an open invitation for sound to travel straight through. To provide effective sound insulation, you need heavy walls, floor and ceiling – the heavier the better. And rather than have one extremely thick wall, build two walls of half the mass with an air gap in between. This 'decoupling' means that a sound wave has to pass through four surfaces rather than two, and a small but significant advantage can be achieved. 'Attention to detail' means that sound will find the smallest gap to get through. No matter how massive your walls, if there is a defect anywhere the degree of sound insulation will be very much reduced.

If you have a choice about where you situate your studio, think about what annoyance value any sound leakage will have. If the room next door happens to be a child's bedroom, you might find yourself having to shut down operations at an early hour, or monitor on headphones. If you are thinking of moving flat or house, look for a property where the potential studio room is as far away from your neighbours as possible. In a semi-detached house for example, the recording room should be at the end of the building, not against the dividing wall between the two houses.

Once you have found the ideal room, or rooms if you are very fortunate or well off, then it's time to start careful planning. The first question you will ask is, 'How much money should I spend on soundproofing?'. I imagine you would like me to reply, 'Not very much', but that wouldn't be true. Good soundproofing is very expensive and it could easily outstrip your entire equipment budget at a home or project studio level. We are going to have to compromise. Near-perfect soundproofing isn't possible unless you have a massive budget to create an equally massive structure. Let's start by looking at the problem areas and see what we can do to improve each in turn.

Floor

Maybe your studio is going to be situated in a downstairs room with a solid floor extending all the way down to mother earth. You lucky person! You would only need to do something to your floor if you were troubled by a nearby railway line or major road. In either of these cases, low frequency vibrations would be very well coupled to the air inside your studio, and from there to the microphones and eventually your ears.

Dealing with a problem of this scale is a major undertaking for which you need to call in the professionals, and your financial advisor. Most of us however will have floorboards whether the studio is upstairs or downstairs. In a downstairs room, the void under the floor may act as a sound transmission path to other parts of the house, but probably not so much to the neighbours'. You may choose to accept this, or you may wish to follow the example of those of us with upstairs studios who are almost bound to have to insulate the floor to some degree.

Floorboards on joists have very little sound insulating capability. The inevitable small gaps between the tongue and groove boards offer an open sound transmission path which we need to block. Since the existing joists are only rated for standard domestic loading, the only complete solution would be to upgrade the structure of the building in a similar manner to a professional loft conversion and add steel supports to bear the weight of a thick concrete floor. Since we are going to have to compromise, then we have to accept that the existing joists will only take a small amount of extra mass and the soundproofing will not be total.

The solution I used when I set up my current home project studio was to use the carpet left by the previous owner of the house, together with some carpet underlay I had brought from my old place, to provide the resilient layer of a basic floating floor, as in Figure 2.1. I didn't bother putting the underlay actually under the carpet since no-one will ever see either again. On top of the carpet and underlay I laid squares of 18mm chipboard, two layers thick, with the joins staggered so that there was no gap for sound to penetrate. Any acoustic designer will tell you that when you go to the trouble of decoupling structures in this way, using a resilient layer, then the worst thing you can do is to 'bridge' the struc-

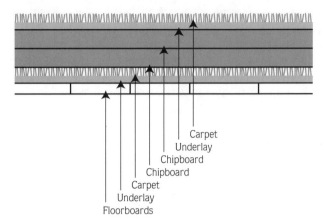

Carpet
Underlay
Chipboard
Chipboard
Carpet
Underlay
Floorboards

Figure 2.1 Simple floating floor

tures. This would have happened if I had screwed the chipboard through to the floorboards so I didn't (I only screwed the two layers together), and also if the chipboard butted directly up against the walls, so I left a gap of about 10mm.

All the gaps, between the chipboard squares and between the chipboard and the walls were filled with mastic. Mastic can be a rubbery or bituminous compound, easily obtained from do-it-yourself merchants, which is used to fill in small gaps, or in some cases it can act as a resilient support in its own right. The rubbery mastic that you can apply with a mastic gun is good for most purposes. On top of the chipboard I placed some more carpet underlay, and finally a carpet. Laying your own carpet isn't too easy, so it might be an idea to call in a professional at this point.

The final result in my case was exactly what I had expected. The degree of insulation through the floor had gone up from practically zero to a level which the rest of the household accepts at all reasonable hours.

Walls

Upgrading the floor in this way brings it up to the standard of an interior wall, just about. You might think that this isn't too wonderful, but bear in mind that most of the leakage in an ordinary house or flat comes through gaps around the doors, and directly through the paper thin doors fitted in most modern properties. I would say that for the average home project studio, you would probably only need to upgrade the wall separating your studio from the neighbours, unless the rest of your family really hate your music! Once again, mass and decoupling are what we need, together with perfect attention to detail. Most professional studios use plasterboard supported by a wooden frame in a style similar to the BBC's famous 'Camden' partition. I have shown in Figures 2.2, 2.3 and 2.4 a double plasterboard partition which would divide two areas quite nicely, but you will probably only wish to construct one layer to add to an existing wall. To build a plasterboard partition yourself isn't as difficult as it looks, or you can always find a jobbing handy person from the classified pages of the local paper. Just make sure you stick around to give the appropriate supervision.

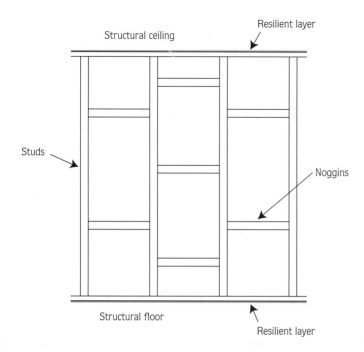

Figure 2.2 Timber frame for plasterboard partition

The wooden frame is built from timber approximately 50mm square. The uprights are called studs, and the horizontal pieces noggins (in England). Since the structure should be decoupled from the rest of the building it is wedged in between resilient layers, probably of hair felt carpet. And try and resist the temptation of rigidly fastening the new structure as much as possible. Each additional nail or screw provides a sound

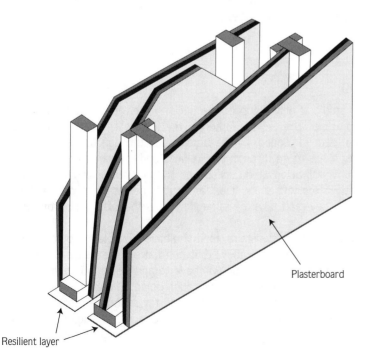

Figure 2.3 Double plasterboard partition

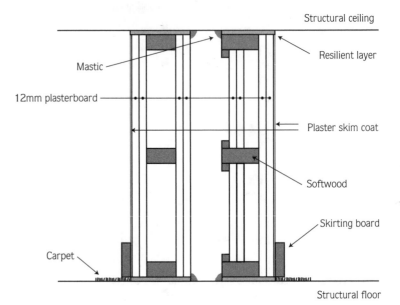

Figure 2.4 Cross section of
double plasterboard partition

transmission path that will reduce the effectiveness of your new partition. The studs should be 600mm apart and the noggins around 1.2m in a staggered pattern. The two layers of plasterboard should also be staggered so that the gaps are not aligned. It is normal practice to tape joins between sheets of plasterboard and lay a thin skim coat of plaster over the entire exposed surface. It is good acoustic practice too to do this. You should fill the space in between the plasterboard with mineral wool to absorb as much as possible any sound passing through. Once again, any small gaps around the edges should be sealed with mastic to prevent sound leaks.

Ceiling

If your studio is at the top of the building then it probably isn't worth doing much to the ceiling. Although the loft space or void above is a potential path for sound, by the time it gets through to the neighbour's property it has to go through two ceilings and the party wall and will be reasonably well attenuated. Laying one thickness of chipboard on top of the joists in the loft is about as far as it is necessary to go, bearing in mind that they can't take the same loading as the joists supporting habitable rooms.

If your studio is downstairs, then you have a problem. You could insulate the floor of the room above, but in a flat or maisonette it might not be part of your property! You will have to add insulation to your ceiling from below, and it will probably be tough going. Choices range from suspended plaster tiles, which are quite good for sound absorption, but will only give around 10dB insulation if you are lucky, through to additional layers of plasterboard, keeping in mind the load bearing capacity of the joists. If you want to be ambitious and you have the height available, then you could fit metal joist hangers to the walls and create a separate structure akin to a Camden partition. You will definitely need an assistant and plenty of DIY skill for this!

Door

Domestic doors are so light that they hardly act as a barrier to sound at all. And what sound doesn't go straight through will easily seep around the edges. The easiest solution is to buy a fire door which will be solid and have much better intrinsic insulation, and fit it into a frame which seals all the way round. For my own studio, I made a door out of two layers of 18mm chipboard with hardwood inserts to support the hinges. I also fitted some extra pieces of wood around the inside of the frame where the door closes, and also at the bottom, to give a good seal all the way round. I used neoprene rubber strip as the actual sealing elements and the result is reasonably good.

Apart from going to the professionals, the next step would be to build a small lobby outside the studio so that a second door could be fitted, and on balance I would recommend this to the do-it-yourselfer in preference to trying to build and hang a really heavy door. Remember that a heavy door needs a heavy frame which needs to be very well fixed to the wall. If you fit the door frame yourself, don't forget to seal around the edges with mastic or this will be another potential sound leakage path.

Windows

Where studio doors are a bit of a problem, windows are a lot easier than you might imagine. The easiest route would be to have conventional double glazing fitted which will provide a little extra sound insulation. For almost complete protection against noisy neighbours (and the reverse) I would recommend purpose made secondary double or even triple glazing. The first thing you will need to do is get used to the idea that you are never going to open your window again. Let's face it, there's no worse window from a sound insulation point of view than an open window! After this, the next step is to measure up the opening very carefully and order some glass. Professional studios use very thick glass which is correspondingly expensive. We are going to use 6mm glass which is thicker than ordinary domestic window glass but not too costly. The details are shown in Figure 2.5 which should be reasonably self explanatory. The essential points to bear in mind are these:

- Don't underestimate how dangerous glass is. Even when it is stored leaning against a wall you could brush against it as you walk by and gash your arm. Even one square metre of 6mm glass will be very difficult to handle alone, so have an assistant, and both of you must wear protective gloves and goggles.
- The glass should be set in mastic so that it is decoupled from the frame.

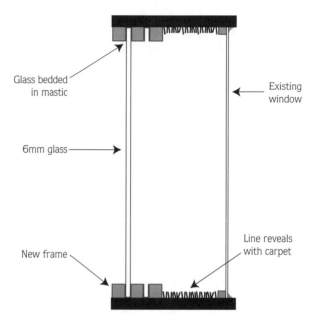

Glass bedded in mastic

Existing window

6mm glass

Line reveals with carpet

New frame

Figure 2.5 Secondary triple glazed window

- Clean the glass meticulously in a good light before you install it. Any dirt or fingerprints you leave behind on the outside will remain there for you and your associates to see for the life of your studio. Put a bit of disinfectant in the water too or you might soon find small circles of fungus growing between the panes.
- Paint or varnish the outside of the secondary glazing frame too. You may think that it won't show, but on a sunny day you will see its reflection in the outer window.
- Line the reveals of the window with carpet, fixed with strong glue, to absorb sound that gets through the panes.
- Once again, treat glass with the utmost respect.

Ventilation

Once you have completely soundproofed your studio, you have completely air proofed it as well! It's easy to forget how much we depend on ventilation through the small gaps between walls and windows and doors. Without ventilation, your studio will quickly become the stuffiest place on earth and two people working in the same room together with heat generating equipment will force the temperature up to unbearable levels, even in the depths of winter. Air conditioning would be nice, but at the very least you need ventilation to bring fresh air into the room and expel stale air out of it. A free standing fan within the room will recirculate the stale air and give you a bit of a breeze but no overall benefit.

In my studio, I cut a hole in the ceiling and fitted an extractor fan up in the loft above. I also cut another hole close to the outside wall so that air can be drawn in from the eaves of the house. Unfortunately, fans are generally quite noisy, so you must take steps to reduce the noise as much as

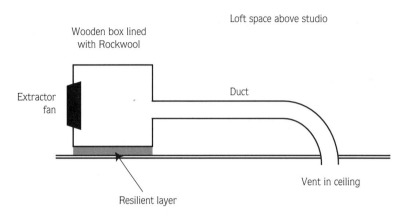

Loft space above studio

Wooden box lined
with Rockwool

Extractor
fan

Duct

Vent in ceiling

Resilient layer

Figure 2.6 Ventilation in the
studio

possible without restricting the air flow. As you can see from Figure 2.6, the fan is mounted in a box which stands on top of a resilient layer, actually some packing material that came with a piece of equipment. Decoupling the fan from the structure of the building makes a big difference to the amount of mechanical noise that gets through. To reduce the noise coming down the duct (which since the fan is an extractor, has to travel against the air flow) I lined the box with mineral wool (the trade name for mineral wool, by the way, is Rockwool and I shall explain more about this in the next chapter). Putting some Rockwool in the duct will reduce the noise very effectively but it also reduces the air flow. Recommendations for ventilation are as follows:

- Use as powerful a fan as you can find. Also, a bigger, slower running fan will be less noisy than a smaller, faster running one.
- Use as large a diameter duct as you can find. The lower the velocity of the air, the less noise will be produced by turbulence.
- You can make a duct from chipboard or MDF (medium density fibreboard). If you line it with Rockwool, even more noise will be absorbed. Make sure that all the joins are well sealed or the fan will suck air through any gaps and not from your studio.
- Don't blow air through or past Rockwool into your studio, unless you want to clog up your equipment and lungs with mineral wool fibres.
- Place the exhaust vent as far as possible from the fresh air intake.
- Bear in mind that noise will escape from your studio through the vents so place them where the noise will do the least harm.

These solutions will transform a significant noise problem into something manageable, but it won't eliminate sound leakage entirely, particularly if you want to record heavy rock bands in your studio! Bear in mind that there is no point in having fantastically good insulation in the walls when the floor and ceiling are not up to scratch. If you want to achieve higher levels of sound insulation, the only sensible solution is to call in a professional acoustic designer. Do-it-yourself is fine up to a point, but if you want to go beyond what I have suggested here then you need professional help otherwise you may spend a lot of money and not achieve the degree of insulation you need.

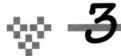

3

Acoustics and layout

It is calculated that the average pro recording engineer travels 1.5 miles every day, moving back and forth from one end of the mixing console to the other. He also spins round in his swivel chair a total of 180,000 degrees in the process of turning to operate the multitrack and turning back again. About 15.5 megajoules of energy are expended in standing up to reach the overhead-mounted outboard FX and sitting down again.

You may think I'm exaggerating for effect, and of course I am. But I know I'm correct in saying that energy wasted on coping with an inefficient system is energy that could be put to good musical use. The average housewife – or househusband – knows full well that a kitchen needs to be well designed, otherwise most of the time spent in cooking is taken up walking from one work area to another. If the kitchen is designed so that the various pieces of equipment are in a logical sequence, then a lot of effort is saved, and you get your dinner sooner!

Unfortunately, there is no such thing as a perfectly designed studio, there are too many conflicting requirements. The BBC Radiophonic Workshop has a circular studio which may come close for one person operation. The layout uses several small mixing consoles rather than one large one so that they can be arranged in an arc with everything within arm's reach. A single conventional console might fit into the room easily enough, but the lone musician/engineer would have to move around much more.

Acoustics also play a role in studio control room layout. As you probably realise, large hard flat surfaces are ideal for reflecting sound. Reflected sound (specular, mirror-like, reflection as opposed to the less harmful diffuse reflection) is one thing we do not want. What a pity that all those effects racks, synth control panels and mixing console surfaces produce reflections in abundance, clouding the wonderfully clear sound coming out of the monitors.

You probably eagerly scan photographs of pro studios for their design ideas and layouts – and so do I. What conclusion do you come to? If you have seen enough studios, then the only conclusion is that the basics are similar, but beyond the basics there are a thousand and one workable studio designs. Most of them do the job of recording music adequately, but the tradeoffs have been made in different ways according to the requirements, and whims, of the studio owner and designer. As always, I am trying to present ideas which you can incorporate into your own scheme of things. The basic plan here I shall keep simple and straightforward.

Acoustic treatment

If you were opening a commercial studio, then you would be engaging an experienced studio designer to put together a scheme for you. Some studio owners have lived to regret the decision to go it alone! But even so, a little knowledge about acoustics is very useful, and we home and project studio owners normally don't have sufficient finance to contract out the design. It is my philosophy on studio acoustics that perfection is unattainable – which should go without saying – but that you can go at least three quarters of the way towards perfection for a fairly reasonable amount of time and money. The law of diminishing returns is working in our favour since it is at the lower end of the scale that the returns are at their highest.

Problems

Enough of the philosophy, now for the practicality. There is only one good kind of sound in a studio, a sound that emerges from the speakers, travels past the engineer's head, and then is either absorbed or breaks up into a zillion vanishingly small reflections. Unfortunately, any flat surface will reflect sound to some degree and any strong reflections will interfere with the direct sound from the speakers causing an uneven frequency response and at the same time distract the engineer from what he/she is meant to be listening to. The frequency response problem is obviously undesirable, but the reason why certain types of reverberation may be undesirable needs further explanation.

Reverberation, the 'dying away' of a sound, is natural to music. Most music is designed to be performed in a reverberant space – military band music being an obvious exception. When you make a recording, you need to be able to judge how much reverberation is on the recording. Excess reverberation in the room will colour your judgment. Another problem with reverberation in the studio control room is that the frequency response of the room itself may not be flat. More than likely, there will be more reverb at bass frequencies. This will make you think that a recording is more bassy than it actually is. What the engineer needs is to be able to judge accurately the sound he is getting. He will then apply his experience to judge what the recording will sound like in a domestic listening room. (I should say that it is not a good idea to record in domestic acoustics on the grounds that a domestic setting is where the recording will be played. Typical living rooms vary considerably in their acoustic qualities. Recordings should be made in rooms which are acoustically as neutral as possible).

Solutions

Now you know the problems, what are the solutions? Well the simplest solution, which will go a long way towards improving your recordings – while not solving all the problems mentioned above – is having carpet on the floor and thick curtaining or more carpet on the walls. By 'thick curtains', I mean thick material and enough of it to hang in very loose folds. Thick curtaining hung with a 50% drape (percentage drape represents

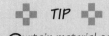

TIP

Curtain material can be quite expensive so your best source might be a secondhand curtain shop (some people seem to like changing their curtains often, and can afford it!) or jumble sale.

the relationship between the width of the wall and the width of the curtain material) will absorb around half of the sound energy that falls upon it. At low frequencies it doesn't work quite as well, but it will definitely have a beneficial effect.

If you want to go further, then Rockwool is the stuff. Rockwool is a fibrous mineral material that builders use for heat insulation (and is usually available from builders' merchants). It is also very good for absorbing sound, and studios use it by the truckload. It needs to be supported by a timber frame and covered with material, but it will absorb nearly 90% of the sound that hits it, and work reasonably well at lower mid frequencies too. Unfortunately, using porous absorption alone inevitably has the effect of reducing reverberation at high and mid frequencies, but leaving the bass end pretty much as it is. The room will now sound dull, and you may be tempted to cut bass on your recordings when it isn't really necessary.

Panel absorbers

To cut low frequency reverberation a different type of absorber is used – a panel absorber. These are really easy to make since they can be just hardboard on thin plywood mounted on a frame against the wall, as in Figure 3.1 The thicker the panel and the greater the air gap, the lower the range of frequencies over which the absorber works, regardless of the area of the panel. If you put some Rockwool in the air gap, then the absorption works over a wider range of frequencies.

You would need an expert to make calculations for you to do the acoustic treatment absolutely properly, but as a rough guide the BBC make modular absorbers similar to simple panel absorbers out of 3mm hardboard with air gaps of about 100mm to 200mm. The greater the area of wall covered with such panel absorbers, the more low frequency energy will be absorbed and you wouldn't go far wrong if you made several panel absorbers with different depths and fixed them around the walls of the room. If you fill them with mineral wool and you drill a series of small holes in the panel then they will absorb mid and high frequencies too. Whether or not you drill the holes, an absorbent filling broadens the range of frequencies over which the absorber is effective from high absorption over a narrow band of frequencies, to a lower degree of absorption over a wider band.

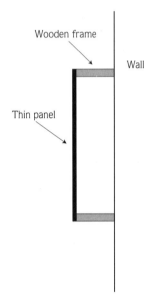

Wooden frame

Wall

Thin panel

Figure 3.1 Panel absorber

What about live rooms?

You may well ask why I'm talking about absorbing sound when a lot of studios are currently going for 'live' rooms and spaces? The answer is that in a small home studio, you are likely to get a better result in a fairly dead acoustic. Reverberation may be beneficial. It certainly will be in the recording area, and a little will help in the control room too. But it certainly works a lot better in large spaces rather than small domestic rooms. Whether the studio is small or large, the one thing reverberation must be is diffused.

As an example consider the difference between a mirror and a sheet of white paper (Figure 3.2). They both reflect most of the light that falls on

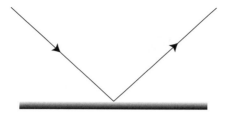

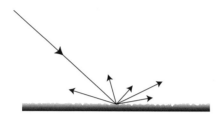

Figure 3.2 Specular and diffused reflections

them, but the mirror reflects in straight lines, forming an image, whereas the paper scatters the light in all directions. It is the same with sound, but specular reflections have the undesirable effects that I mentioned earlier. Diffuse reflections do not. The trouble is that it is not so easy to diffuse sound properly as it is to absorb it. Sound can have long wavelengths, so for a surface to be acoustically rough (as the paper is optically) it needs to have roughness with large dimensions. An easy way of providing a combination of absorption and diffusion is to build some bookshelves and put on them all those impressive volumes you bought but never quite got around to reading. The books are reasonably good absorbers, and their varying dimensions provides an acoustically rough surface for good diffusion of whatever energy isn't absorbed.

Studio layout

Now we can think about putting some gear into the room, but we must start with the basics. The real fundamental factor is that you have to have two loudspeakers to hear the music in stereo, and you have to be there to do the listening. Too simple? Not really, because this is the foundation from which everything else will grow. Figure 3.3 shows the relative positioning. Remembering your school maths, you will recognise this as an equilateral triangle. This gives the best compromise between width of the stereo image and localisation of panned instruments. If you don't believe me – and there is no written law to say that you have to have things this way – then try it out, preferably in your by now acoustically favourable room. The speakers will need to be positioned so that they sit symmetrically between the walls of the room, otherwise the stereo image will be distorted as I mentioned earlier. Normally they are positioned against one wall, but there is no reason why they couldn't be on opposite sides of a

TIP

However you do the acoustic treatment, try as much as possible to make it symmetrical about the left/right axis, otherwise the uneven reflections will tempt you to unbalance the stereo image in the speakers to 'compensate'. It may sound right in your room, but it will be wrong on the tape.

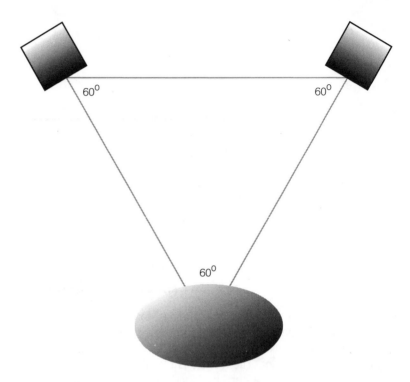

Figure 3.3 Optimum listening position

diagonal in a square room – at the expense of some wasted space.

Speakers are sensitive to how close they are positioned to reflecting surfaces. The problem is that all loudspeakers tend to radiate sound in all directions – omnidirectionally – at low frequencies. This sound reflects from nearby boundaries and, if the boundary is within half a sound wavelength at some frequency in the audible range, then all frequencies lower than this will tend to be boosted. It may sound like a good thing to get some extra bass for nothing, but it usually has the result of making the speaker sound 'boomy'. You would tend to compensate for this by putting less bass on your recordings.

Most hi-fi speakers and near field studio monitors are designed to operate best in 'free field' conditions and need to be positioned as far away from walls as the available space will allow. Some studio monitors are designed to be mounted on a boundary, or inset into it. But not in the typical home or project studio price bracket. Some nearfield monitors are meant to be stood on top of a large mixing console, and they actually sound best that way.

The general conclusion on speaker positioning is mount them symmetrically as far away from the walls as space will allow. Don't forget that the floor and the ceiling are boundaries too. Mount the speakers halfway between floor and ceiling pointing down at your ears for best results. When you have a paper design, go into the room with CD player, amp and speakers and try it out. It's worth spending quite a bit of time getting the right speaker placement and the right listening position.

Equipment layout

I have spent more time scratching my head over equipment layout over the years than any other problem in my home project studio. The trouble is that there seems to be no ideal solution for one person studio operation. Bear in mind that the engineer/musician is operating a mixing console, keyboard, synth modules, effects, multitrack, stereo tape recorder, sequencer, and probably a few other things at the same time. 'At the same time' is the key phrase, because apart from the stereo recorder used for the final mix, all of the other equipment is in use all the time. You end up bobbing about from one piece of equipment to another. There's no studio layout to suit all circumstances, but let's have a look at the example of a keyboard playing recordist who wants to work quickly and effectively from a fixed position.

Keyboard player layout

The first problem our keyboard orientated recordist will have to face in laying out the studio is whether to have the master keyboard or the mixing console in front of the speakers. Of course, pro studios always have the console in front of the speakers, because that is where the engineer sits. The keyboard player can go somewhere else, probably to a less than optimum listening position. When you are the engineer and the keyboard player you have a dilemma. Do you want the best quality sound when you are track laying, or when you are mixing? For many people, mixing will win out. But there are advantages the other way. For one thing, it is much more inspirational to hear the best quality sound from the optimum listening position while you are recording. Or why not have two pairs of speakers and a conveniently placed switch so that you can have the best of both worlds?

Let's say you have opted to have the console in front of the speakers. Now where do you put the keyboard? To the left of the console? To the right? In parallel with it so you have to turn right round to play? I'll go for the left, at right angles to the console. I choose this option because it gives me easy access to the input channels of the console, which are conventionally situated on the left, and they will be in use together with the keyboard as the recording progresses. The computer sequencer will go nicely behind and above the keyboard. Next comes the sampler and synth module rack, assuming you have these items. This has to be very close to the keyboard. If you need to edit the sounds as the recording progresses, and let's assume that you are an adventurous swashbuckling recordist, you will need to be able to plonk the keys with one hand while you tweak the expander with the other. There is no substitute for having these two within an armspan! If this is so obvious, why do some people have set-ups where it can't be done?

The armspan factor dictates that the expander rack is facing the monitors. It is probably a good idea to look at Figure 3.4 now. I haven't shown it in the sketch, but the expander modules really ought to be at keyboard

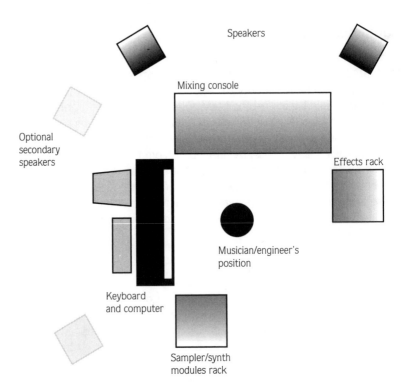

Speakers

Mixing console

Optional
secondary
speakers

Effects rack

Musician/engineer's
position

Keyboard
and computer

Figure 3.4 Equipment layout
for a solo keyboard recordist

Sampler/synth
modules rack

height plus, or if they are lower than the keyboard then consider angling
them upwards. It is no use having to squat to get at awkward-to-adjust
machinery. Place things like power amps and other equipment that you
can set and forget at the bottom of your racks. The right hand side of the
console is still vacant, so it looks like a good place for the effects rack and
patchbay. Once again, preferably this should be positioned so you will not
have to bend down. Apart from equipment that you can more or less set-
and-forget, the patchbay should be the lowest thing in the rack. Why?
Because the patchcords will droop all over the controls you need to get at
if it isn't. Only put equipment below the patchbay that you know you will
use less often than the patchbay.

Does it work acoustically?

When you have decided on the layout and have a pretty good idea of how
you want things operationally, it's a good idea to go back and consider the
set up acoustically. Remember that the hard flat surfaces of the equipment cause the kind of reflections that we don't want. Since we can't
make the equipment itself absorbent (although we can do something for
the sides of the racks), the only option we have is to make sure that the
reflections don't go anywhere harmful – i.e. into your ears. If you draw a
precisely dimensioned diagram, you can draw in the path followed by the
direct sound coming from the speakers. Remember that sound reflects at
the same angle at which it strikes a surface and you will be able to draw
the pattern of reflections. Are any of them hitting the engineer's ears?
Then angle the equipment so that the reflections aim into a more remote

part of the studio. This is not audio black magic but a way of fine-tuning the sound of a room by very simple methods – and you can't say that it costs any money to consider how your equipment is angled.

By now, as long as your console isn't too wide, you should have a system which you can operate without leaving your comfortable seat. I haven't included the positioning of the multitrack, but it could be worked into the set-up quite easily, or you could put your hand in your pocket and buy a remote control (why don't they come with infra red remotes like TVs and videos?).

If the layout I have devised doesn't suit your studio arrangements, then I hope that the procedure I have followed, considering how the acoustics and the different pieces of equipment interact, will help you work out your own layout plans more easily. Every set up involves weighing up compromises between acoustics, convenience and versatility. Make one factor better and it is likely the other two will suffer. Think carefully about how you want to work in your studio and you will get the compromise that suits you best.

4

Studio furniture and decor

'A set up, not a lash up'

Whenever I visit a top class pro studio, I always get a very comfortable and relaxed feeling as soon as I enter the control room. This is due to the fact that top studios recognise the importance of a neat equipment installation and well designed decor to the customer paying an hourly rate. Go into the average project studio, even some owned by top musicians, and you will find equipment stacked up like the Leaning Tower of Pisa and cables tangled together all over the place like a massive nest of serpents. Which do you think is more conducive to musical productivity? OK, I know some people work best among clutter, but I think such people are the exception rather than the rule. I know that I like my studio to be the equivalent of an artist's blank canvas when I enter it on a morning. Everything is where it should be, it works properly without any setting up or messing about, and I can get as creative as I want and make as much mess as I like during my musically productive day. Then, even though I am naturally an untidy person, I tidy up my studio ready for the next session because I know that's the way I can work best.

Figure 4.1 shows my home project studio. I'm not suggesting that you ought to imitate it, or even like it, but I have a few ideas that I think you will find useful in making your own studio an efficient working environment.

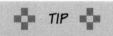

TIP

If you have the opportunity of looking inside a TV outside broadcast truck, grab it! The people that design OB vehicles are masters of the art of getting a lot into a small space (and sound always gets a much smaller space than picture!).

Size...

...isn't everything of course, but it helps if you can have a room at least 4 metres square. In this space, you and one other person will be comfortable, you and two other people will be just about OK. If you want to add any significant amount of acoustic treatment then bear in mind that you will have to lose 100mm or so from each surface. If you want to add soundproofing and acoustic treatment, then 300mm could easily be lost, possibly more. That's why I chose to cover the walls of my studio with carpet tiles, which are not ideal acoustically but I didn't want to lose any more space. My ceiling is fibreboard on wooden joists so there is quite a bit of low frequency absorption up there anyway. If you plan on accommodating your studio in a smaller space, then I would advise you to go

Figure 4.1 The author's home
project studio

and see some yachts and caravans and see how a lot of things can be fitted into a small space with a bit of ingenuity.

Decoration

The look of your studio will be important. It should be a comfortable
place to work, and it should be reasonably impressive to visiting musicians
or producers. Most of all, it should look totally unlike any part of your
domestic environment. Working at home is more difficult than people
imagine until they try it. One of the biggest psychological problems is getting the feeling that you are really at work, when everything around you
is telling you that you are at home! I'm not a designer, but I looked
around to gather ideas on how I could make my studio into a pleasant
working environment without spending too much money. It isn't shown in
the photo, but I have a ceiling painted black with a wooden trellis suspended beneath it, which is something you would never find in a domestic
room. I got the idea from an Italian restaurant (I wonder if I can claim the
bill against my tax?).

There are design ideas all around if you keep your eyes open. As far as
the walls are concerned, the carpet tiles were practical but I felt I needed
something a little more interesting. It occurred to me that when I am mixing, I need something to allow my eyes to alight upon without having so
much visual distraction that my attention is taken away from the music.
The bland pattern of the rug works just fine, and since it's about an inch
thick it provides extra acoustic absorption too. The rug hangs from metal
rings sewn into the backing hooked onto twelve screws fixed into the
wall.

Furniture

It's easy enough to buy a stand or a table to put the mixer on, and order metal equipment racks from a catalogue, but this is almost certainly the easiest way to achieve the appearance of a lash-up. If you want your studio to look good, then building your own furniture is the best option – and it's really not all that difficult.

The first part of the procedure is deciding what your needs are in terms of equipment accommodation. I use a core of equipment which I supplement by hiring when necessary, so I don't own all that much gear. If I wanted to acquire more, I would move the less used items into another rack out of the way. 19 inch rack mounting audio equipment comes in packages a certain number of units, or U, high. An effects unit might be 1U and a sampler 3U. 1U is equal to 1³/₄ inches or 44.5mm. For my patchbay and equipment I reckoned that two 16U racks would be just about right.

Coincidentally, they are also just the right height to fit a shelf in between and stand the mixing console on top! I made a slight blunder when I cut the hole for the stereo tape recorder and there isn't enough room to put the patchbay at the top of the right hand rack. That's something I'll fix when I need that extra space. I'm sure you have noticed by now that my studio doesn't quite look like the layout I described in Chapter 3, but that's because I'm not totally keyboard orientated and I need my studio to be more versatile, especially if I am working with other musicians. One day I'll have a dedicated keyboard room too!

Building a rack

The first part of the rack building procedure is to think long and hard about what it should be like in all respects. The design of the rack will more or less be dictated by the equipment and ancillaries you intend to put in it – leaving a bit of room for future expansion. Also essential food for thought is how exactly you are going to build it. The way the panels fit together can have designed-in ease of construction, and my feeling about any form of do-it-yourself is that a little effort in the planning stage can design out any vast requirement for woodworking skill.

Let's start first with what to put in the rack. A quick list will include MIDI modules, effects units, patchbay, and possibly a DAT or a cassette deck. Start with the vertical dimension and add up the number of units (U's) of rack space you currently require. Add a bit for future expansion and 2U at the bottom for luck. The width of the rack is of course 19 inches plus a bit for the thickness of the wood, so that is not a matter for too much deliberation. The depth of the rack, however, is very important. The key piece of information necessary is the dimension of the deepest piece of rack equipment you may acquire at some time in the future. The Guinness Book of Records doesn't provide a category for this. However, the prize for any equipment ever installed in my rack went to a sampler with a magnificent rack penetration of 16 inches (about 400mm). Of course, this means 16 inches plus space for connectors – jack plugs and mains connectors. Having been restricted in the past by a just-deep-enough rack, I would recommend an extra four inches (100mm) added to the maximum depth of the rack equipment.

Tools and materials

You don't need much in the way of carpentry tools to put a rack together, not a basic rack like this one anyway. If you have a small hand saw, an electric drill with 3mm and countersink bits, a jigsaw and perhaps a circular saw, you will find construction very straightforward. A cross head screwdriver and a small hammer will come in handy too.

The basic constructional material is chipboard. It's not exactly the king of woods, but it is very user-friendly and relatively cheap. MDF (Medium Density Fibreboard) and plywood are good too, but more expensive. Where you should buy your wood is good question. In my experience, a good local source of timber in small quantities is not so easy to come by. What's needed is a supplier who stores his wood out of the rain and will cut the wood to size for you (to an accuracy of a couple of millimetres).

The first requirement is fairly obvious. Working with bent chipboard is not fun. The second is a little more difficult. Get an estimate of the price first, because some suppliers don't like cutting tiny (to them) pieces, and bump up the price accordingly. For the type of rack I am describing, £30 to £40 should amply cover the cost. DIY hypermarkets will often cut wood to size, but they may have restrictions on how many cuts you can have per sheet.

For a rack like this, it's best to use 18mm (³/₄ inch) thickness chipboard, high density for preference. 12mm (¹/₂ inch) chip is OK, but with the thicker variety you can get away without using battens (supporting pieces of timber) which makes the job easier. To cover the end grain of the wood (if you can say that chipboard has a grain) some lengths of 18mm by 6mm wood strip are ideal. Make sure it's straight when you buy it! The only other materials are Evostik 'Resin W' glue (I can confirm their claim that it's stronger than the wood itself), 50mm and 12mm or 15mm number 8 chipboard screws, and some small panel pins. Oh yes, a bit of sandpaper will smooth things off nicely before finishing.

Apart from the carpentry supplies there is one hardware item that you need to buy from a studio supplier – a length of rack strip. Rack strip is a piece of plated steel angle, punched to the exact specifications of a 19 inch rack. All you do is cut off the right length with a hacksaw, and screw it onto your rack. You can even have this cut to size if you like. The sort I use gives the correct spacing if the supporting panels are 19 ¹/₈ inch apart – check this with the supplier of the strip that you buy. Add to this a quantity of M6 screws and cage nuts for mounting your gear when the rack is finished.

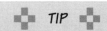

TIP

There may be other design considerations. Do you want castors? They make it easy to shift the rack around, but add extra unproductive height. Do you have any non-rack mounting equipment – such as a power amplifier or mixer power supply – that you would like to hide away in the rack. These all add extra U's. The list could go on, but the answer of course is to make a list of all the possible problems, and then you can think logically about how to solve them. It will not be impossible.

Materials you will need

Electric drill
3mm drill bit
Countersink bit
Small hand saw
Jigsaw
Circular saw (unless you have the panels cut for you)
Hacksaw (or have the rack strip cut to length)
Small hammer
Cross head screwdriver to suit chipboard screws
Brush for paint or varnish
18mm chipboard
18mm x 6mm edging strip
Evostik Resin W glue
50mm No. 8 chipboard screws
12mm or 15mm No. 8 chipboard screws
Panel pins
Sandpaper (fine)
Paint or varnish
Masking tape

Let's get to work!

Every do-it-yourselfer finds their own way of putting wood together. I use a pair of Workmate type benches to support one panel while I'm fixing another one to it, but you can easily get by without. Rather than give you a blow by blow account of how to put the rack together, I'll leave it mostly up to your own ingenuity but mention a few important points that will save you getting it wrong if it's your first time.

- Don't forget to make the opening between the side panels slightly wider than 19 inches, according the specifications of the manufacturer of the rack strip.
- The holes in the rack strip will probably follow a spacing pattern narrow-wide-wide-narrow-wide-wide etc. Cut the strip just outside of one of the the narrow space between the holes so that you have a whole number of U. If you hope to make two shorter strips out of one long one, bear in mind that 1U will be wasted. When you examine the strip carefully and hold it against a piece of equipment, this will all become obvious.
- Fix the edging strip with glue and panel pins. Once you have painted or varnished the strip the pins will be almost unnoticeable. Unless you have a good mitre saw, it's best to cut the strip a little longer than you need, fix it on and wait for the glue to dry before cutting it to the precise length. Don't forget to allow for the dimensions of the edging strip when working out the size of your panels.
- Although chipboard is strong enough to take the weight of your equipment when the pressure is applied vertically down a panel,

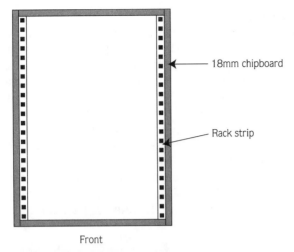

18mm chipboard

Rack strip

Front

Figure 4.2 Front of rack

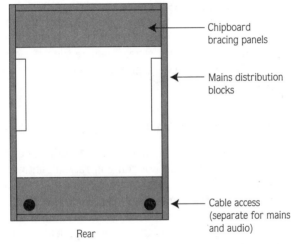

Chipboard
bracing panels

Mains distribution
blocks

Cable access
(separate for mains
and audio)

Rear

Figure 4.3 Back of rack

chipboard is pretty weak in every other respect. That's why special chipboard screws are necessary, and why it's preferable to use fairly long ones that have a greater contact area with the wood. When fixing the side of one panel to the edge of another, you may need to drill a pilot hole all the way through otherwise the wood that you are screwing into may bulge. Take care to guide the screw in at precisely the right angle or it will burst out of the wood. With this method of construction the screw heads will show. You will probably not even notice them, but if you would prefer that they didn't then you can countersink the screws well into the wood and use wood filler on top. A good book on DIY will tell you about other ways to conceal screws.

- Varnish is a suitable finish for chipboard, surprisingly enough, but it takes a lot of coats, rubbing down with fine sandpaper between each coat. I used chestnut coloured varnish which by the time I had applied sufficient coats became almost black. If you buy a brush that is guaranteed not to shed bristles you will save yourself a lot of trouble. The edging strip can be varnished in a contrasting colour either before fixing or by using masking tape after the rack is finished.

Mains supply

Every now and then you see the headline 'Musician killed by live microphone', or something similar. Usually it's in some dodgy club where the mains wiring is in an unsatisfactory condition. The one essential thing in the home studio is to eliminate the possibility of this happening, so proper mains wiring is essential. The ideal solution is to get a qualified electrician to install extra sockets on the ring main in your studio, one per piece of equipment subject to the maximum allowable on the ring. The other acceptable solution is to use commercially available multiway mains blocks. Usually they have four sockets each and plug in to one socket on the wall. These ought to be unplugged from the mains when not in use, and must not be 'daisy chained'.

Please bear in mind that however you arrange your mains supply, make absolutely sure that it is safe.

Rack bolts and cage nuts

To fix your equipment in the rack, you will need a supply of cage nuts. These are square M6 size nuts in a springy steel surround. They clip into the square holes in the rack strip. To mate with the cage nuts, chrome plated M6 screws will give a nice finish. Use nylon washers to avoid scratching your equipment. These items are available from studio suppliers.

Rack mounting non-rack mounting equipment

There are several pieces of equipment available that you may like to use in your home studio which do not come in rack mounting form. Often the manufacturer of the equipment or a third party manufacturer makes a rack mounting kit, but sometimes it is possible to adapt these units yourself so that they can be rack mounted with the rest of the gear.

One such unit is the Quad 306 power amplifier. The unit is constructed so that the front panel and chassis carry all the components. The body of the unit is merely a sleeve which screws onto the chassis. To rack mount a Quad 306, or any other unit that is constructed in a similar way, you need a blank 19 inch panel with a cut-out slightly smaller than the unit's frontal area. Also, with some equipment you may need holes for the front panel mounting screws. The blank 19 inch panel is simply sandwiched between the unit's front panel and the body sleeve. Each piece of equipment has its own mounting problems which you will have to sort out. Pro studios often make up panels like this to handle requirements that can't be met by simply buying equipment off-the-shelf.

Figure 4.4 A Quad 306 amplifier mounted on a 19 inch panel

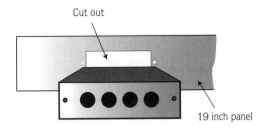

Cut out

19 inch panel

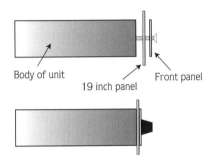

Body of unit

19 inch panel

Front panel

Figure 4.5 Rack mounting
non-rack mounting equipment

Installing the equipment

Installing rack equipment single handed is a tough job. You need to hold
the equipment while you screw it into position and there is a risk that you
might bend the flanges. The easy way is to install the equipment from the
bottom up. That way, you will always have something to rest the equipment on while you screw it in firmly.

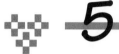

5

Cables and connectors

When the cable-free studio is invented, as one day it must be, we shall be free of one of the greatest sources of annoyance to the studio owner or musician. Until that day arrives (don't hold your breath) we must find ways to minimise the problems that a multiplicity of cables can bring.

In case you haven't had the pleasure of getting tangled up in cables yet, here are some of the difficulties that can crop up:

- Unreliable connections
- Incorrect routing between equipment
- Interference
- Loss of high frequencies
- Knotted or tangled cables
- Cables underfoot

Some of these difficulties may seem trivial in the clear light of day. But when you can't figure out what is plugged into what halfway through an all-night session, then the gnashing of teeth and tearing out of hair have to be taken as symptoms of a blood pressure raised to unhealthily high levels. It's not good for the music either. There are several levels of sophistication in studio cabling ranging from no cabling system at all – just a bag full of leads – to a full patchbay system with cabling in trunking or conduit. I'll be describing sensible systems in a later chapter but for now, I'll stick to the cables themselves. How they are constructed, and what the advantages and disadvantages of each type are.

Mythology

Usually when someone is spouting their opinions on the subject of cables, it's in an article in a hifi magazine and they are going on about 'linear crystal' and 'oxygen free' and other such mysteries. I have to go along with the man who founded one of the world's most important mixing console manufacturing companies when he said that if people thought they could hear a difference, that was OK with him. I think there is enough to worry about, getting the basic engineering principles right to make sure that measurable – and clearly audible – deficiencies of cables are minimised. The difference you will make to your sound by moving a microphone an inch is a thousand times the difference in changing

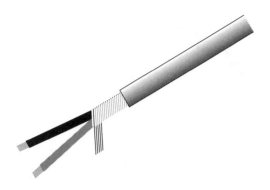

Figure 5.1a Lapped screen twin cable

between 'ordinary' cable and one of the esoteric types. Choosing the correct cable is a straightforward matter once you know what the requirements are. Let's take a look at Figure 5.1a, which shows a two conductor audio cable.

As you can see, there are several components. Each signal conductor is made of a number of fine strands of copper. Around each signal conductor is a layer of plastic insulation – often one is coloured red and the other black. Around the two signal conductors are more fine strands of copper – known as the screen. Keeping the inside in and the outside world out is another layer of plastic insulation. This type of cable is known as a 'lapped screen twin' cable. Get out your microscope and look at the fine detail...

The signal conductors each consist of between 20 and 60 copper strands, each approximately 0.1mm in diameter. The material is copper because it is a good electrical conductor, and also easy for the manufacturer to form into a wire. There is a large number of thin strands because this is a more physically flexible arrangement than having just one thick strand. If there were, say, 30 strands 0.1 mm in diameter, the conductor would be simply described as 30/0.1 mm.

The insulation around the signal conductors is typically PVC, although other plastic materials may be used. The screen consists of 50 or 60 strands of copper wire, each once again about 0.1mm in diameter. When it is wound round and round the signal conductors, it is called a 'lapped' screen. When the strands are woven together it is known as a 'braided' screen, as shown in Figure 5.1b. The screen is normally connected to earth and keeps electrical interference away from the signal conductors.

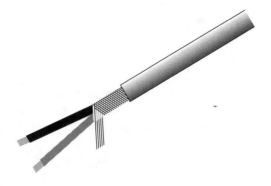

Figure 5.1b Braided screen twin cable

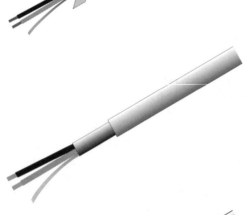

Figure 5.1c Foil screen twin (FST) cable

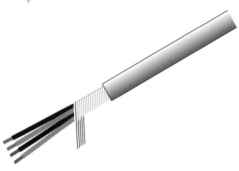

Figure 5.1d Conductive plastic screen twin cable

Figure 5.1e Lapped screen quad cable

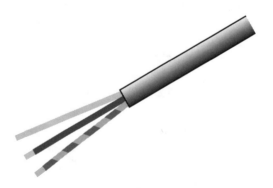

Figure 5.1f Mains cable

The outer insulator is PVC once more, and the overall diameter is about 6mm. This is a standard audio cable and is colloquially known simply as 'mic' cable, although it can equally well be used for line level sources.

Figure 5.1c shows Foil Screen Twin or FST, an installation cable which is described later. Figure 5.1d is a conductive plastic screen mic cable which uses electrically conducting plastic for the screen rather than copper wire. Since you can't solder to plastic there is a 'drain' wire running along the wire in contact with the screen which should be connected to earth. Figure 5.1e is 'quad' cable which is used for the ultimate in interference rejecting cables, and Figure 5.1f is good old fashioned 13 amp mains cable which is often used for connecting up speakers, although even thicker conductors would be preferable.

Now we know about the construction, what else is there to know about cables? One significant feature of audio cables is 'capacitance'. Capacitance in a cable can be compared to holes in a hose pipe. When you water the lawn, most of the liquid comes out of the end of the hose as it should, but some leaks out of the hose, along its length, into the ground. In the cable, some of the electricity in the signal conductor can leak through to the screen, which is of course connected to electrical ground. It is always the high frequencies that are first to get through, so if you had a long cable of high conductor to screen capacitance, you could expect to get a dull sound. There is also capacitance from conductor to conductor which has precisely the same effect. These two characteristics are measurable and must be included in the specification of a cable. Reasonably low capacitance is obviously desirable. Cables also possess electrical resistance and inductance, but these don't really have too much significance in the lengths of cable typically used in a home studio. If you were laying a transatlantic telephone cable the situation would be different.

This is probably as good a time as any to examine why there are two conductors in this cable instead of just one conductor and a screen. In professional audio, it is normal to use balanced connections between equipment. Balanced wiring reduces hum and interference and makes it simple to connect any piece of equipment to any other without the likelihood of problems arising. It costs more, but pros are prepared to make that initial investment because it saves time and money in the long run. The balanced system works by having the same signal in both conductors, but one inverted in polarity – a bit like a battery connected the other way round. Balanced equipment has transformers, or the electronic equivalent, which sort everything out at both input and output. The advantage is that any interference that gets into the cable is cancelled out in the balancing/unbalancing process.

I don't want to delve too deeply into the whys and wherefores of balancing right now, we'll take a look at that later in Chapter 8. What I do want to point out is that there is no such thing as balanced cable. It's the equipment that is balanced, and two conductor cable is suitable for use with balanced equipment. It is also suitable for use with unbalanced equipment, as found in the home studio. But this is getting off the basic subject of the cables themselves, so it will have to wait until later.

More on cable capacitance

If you buy cable from a reputable pro audio dealer (not a hifi shop or hardware merchant) then you shouldn't have any noticeable problems with capacitance, unless you have really long cable runs (100 m or more). Digital signals are another matter. They are much higher in frequency and are therefore much more subject to the effects of capacitance. There are two main digital audio connection standards: S/PDIF and AES/EBU. Although the idea of both is that they can be used with standard audio cables (AES/EBU is balanced), practice has proved that this is not always the case. For digital signals, buy special low capacitance digital signal cable from a pro audio dealer and keep the lengths of the cable to a minimum. Remember that guitar leads are different to normal audio cables. They too need to be low in capacitance, but they also need to be non-microphonic. If you use a normal audio cable, or even a digital audio cable, as a guitar lead, you might find that it crackles when it is moved.

Cable mechanics

The mechanical properties of a cable are as important as the electrical properties. Ever had one of those cables that can tie itself into a knot without human intervention? We all have, and we know that it is something to avoid. The types of mic cables I described above are suitable for everyday use in the studio – cables that you would connect for a particular purpose then disconnect and coil up for storage. The two features that make them good for this application are flexibility and coilability. Flexibility comes from the fine stranded wire used, and also from the soft plastic insulation. Coilability – I don't think it's a scientifically measurable quantity – comes from the relationship between the flexibility of the cable and its diameter. There is a point where a cable can be too flexible and too small in diameter for its own good, and creates the knotty problem described above. Six or seven millimetres is a good diameter for a mic cable.

Cables of lesser diameter can be used for installation work. That is where the cable will be wired up and left undisturbed for evermore, so it doesn't matter what its handling properties are like as long as it's reasonably easy to hook up in the first place. You won't touch it after that. There are two types of cable that I find very useful for installation. The first, I use basically because it's cheap. There's nothing wrong with that as long as it is electrically OK. It is a single conductor cable (therefore only suitable for unbalanced connections) with a 7/0.2mm signal conductor and a lapped screen. The overall diameter is 3mm and the cost is a mere 15p or so per metre. Its big advantage is that it is ideal for making into a loom. A loom, as you are probably aware, is a collection of 20 or 30 individual cables fastened together and all going to the same place. I'll be explaining how to make one in the next chapter.

My other favourite installation cable is known as FST, standing for Foil Screen Twin (Figure 5.1c). The brand I use is available with two 7/0.2mm conductors. But instead of having a copper wire screen, it has an aluminium foil screen. To connect the screen to earth there is a drain wire, which is an uninsulated 7/0.2mm wire in electrical contact with the screen throughout the length of the cable. It is actually a much better cable than the one I described above, having a lower capacitance, making it good for use in long runs. It is of course more expensive, around 30p per metre in 100m lengths. FST cable is fairly stiff, which makes it easier to install inside racks. The one thing you can't do with FST cable is to use it as you would an ordinary mic cable. It tends to kink and would soon become difficult to work with.

Practicalities

So you are wiring up a studio and need some cable. What types of cable do you need? I would urge you to investigate all the possibilities before deciding for yourself what to use. But once you have found cables that suit your purposes, stick to them. Being consistent can save a lot of time and energy, but whatever you do, avoid unbranded cables. There is little saving to be made, and the operation of your entire studio depends on these bits of copper and plastic.

For mic cable (remembering that this is the accepted term for cables that follow the use-then-coil-and-store routine) you should invest in 100m of lapped screen twin at around 60p to £1 per metre. Or if you are prepared to forego a discount for quantity, you could get ten 10m lengths in different colours which is a great help in finding your way around a bird's nest of cables on the studio floor. For studio use, braided screen or quad cable is unnecessarily expensive, but if you intend making recordings anywhere that lighting dimmers are active, then the better quality cable will keep you just that little bit further away from the horrendous interference they often produce. The two installation cables are Medium Single Round (what a name!) – that is the cheap cable I described above – that is available from a company called Electromail, and FST which is available from most studio suppliers.

Funnily enough, the one kind of cable I have little use for is multicore cable. This type of cable consists of several – perhaps as many as 32 – individual two conductor plus screen cables, surrounded by one outer jacket. Much of the professional sound industry thrives on multicore cable, so why isn't it suitable for a home studio? Most types of multicore are intended for use with multipin connectors. It isn't possible to fix the individual inner cables to phono, jack or XLR connectors as they are not, by themselves, mechanically robust enough to be exposed to the outside world. They need to remain snug in their outer insulation, or inside the hard shell of a multipin connector.

The most likely place you will find a multipin connector in your studio is on the back of a digital multitrack recorder, but you will find it a lot easier just to use the jacks or phono connectors the manufacturers also provide. Some multicore cables have inner cables which can be split up and attached to individual connectors. But multicore cables are stiff and heavy and they could impose an excessive strain on a feeble phono. Also, when you work out the cost, you don't save much by going for multicore. It's much better to gather together individual cables into a loom.

Trunking

How do you install hundreds of metres of cables in a studio without making a horrible tangled mess out of them? The answer is that all cables apart from your ten or so mic cables should be installed in trunking so that they are permanently out of sight and out of harm's way. Many studios use skirting trunking where, instead of having a solid strip of wood as a skirting board, as in flats and houses, the skirting is hollow so that cables can be installed inside. I would recommend that you make a skirting trunking as shown in Figure 5.2. You won't get past a door very easily, but you will still probably be able to get your cables anywhere in the room totally invisibly.

If, like in my studio, your equipment occupies an island site in the

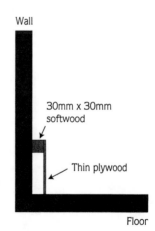

Wall

30mm x 30mm softwood

Thin plywood

Floor

Figure 5.2 Skirting trunking keeps cables out of sight

centre of the room, then you should pass the cables under the floor-boards. This needs a little planning at the stage of laying a floating floor. Make sure that holes are cut in all the right places, and poke a length of thick string through where the cables will eventually go. You will need some stiff wire or something similar to do this. When you eventually come to installing your cables, all you have to do is tape them to the string and pull. Tape another length of string to the cables and pull that through for when you have more cables to install.

Cable storage

Cables get very chummy when they are stored together, and like to inter-twine themselves, making it difficult for you to sort them out. Here are three methods of keeping them separate:

1　Hang them on coat hooks, sticking strictly to the rule 'one hook – one cable'.
2　Use a short loop of rope like that shown in Figure 5.3 and hang several on each hook.
3　When you coil a cable, wrap a short length of masking tape around it. You can hang it on a hook, bung it in a box, or store it any way you like and your cables stay tidy.

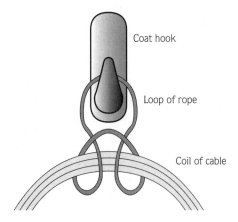

Coat hook

Loop of rope

Coil of cable

Figure 5.3 How to hang several cables on one coat hook without them getting tangled

Connectors

I have mentioned connectors a few times already, and you have probably already come across the main types. The three most common connectors are the XLR, jack and phono. For your MIDI connections you will also come across the five pin DIN. XLR connectors are what the pros use. In fact, professionals turn their noses up at equipment that doesn't have XLRs on the back because they think it's a sign of poor quality. This isn't always the case, as lower cost equipment may have excellent facilities and sound quality but compromises have to be made somewhere. Let's see what the pros and cons are.

Figure 5.4 The four types of
3-pin XLR connector

XLR connectors

XLRs come in four types: cable male, cable female, panel male and panel female. You can tell male and female apart by looking for certain obvious features and making a comparison with the human body! XLRs used for most audio signal connections have three pins, although the same type of connector is available with up to seven pins. The advantages of the XLR are that it is normally robust; it's easy to solder since there is plenty of room inside; connection is usually latching and therefore reliable; the three pins can carry a balanced signal.

Jack connectors

Jack connectors can be every bit as good as XLRs, although they rarely latch and the cable clamp isn't usually as firm, but the real problem is that there are so many rogue manufacturers producing cheap ones that really are not usable. A stereo jack can be used to carry a single balanced signal so there's no restriction on that count.

Phono connectors

The phono connector, also known as the cinch connector or RCA jack, is the least good of the three. It is small and often fiddly to wire. The cable clamp is never any good and the two contacts can only carry an unbalanced signal. Having said that, a number of manufacturers are now producing very high quality phono connectors that make the best of an intrinsically bad design. Two things to look out for are the maximum cable diameter a phono connector can accommodate, and that some higher quality phonos have too great a barrel diameter to insert a pair into adjacent sockets on typical equipment.

MIDI connectors

Are there any connectors that you should avoid soldering yourself? Yes, never solder a MIDI connector. The five pin DIN connector is so small and fiddly that I reckon only one sound engineer in ten could solder it properly. It is more difficult even than patchbay wiring. I would recommend either that you buy MIDI leads ready assembled, or that if you need to extend one then you cut a shorter one into two and splice an extra length in between. Be careful how you insulate the bare wires at the joins, or use pairs of XLR connectors. If you really do want to make up your own MIDI cables, note that pin 2 is the screen, pins 4 and 5 carry the data.

6

Soldering techniques and wiring looms

There's no getting away from it. If you are a home studio builder, then sooner or later you are going to have to solder. And unless you like tangled cables, you will need to be able to make up your own wiring looms. To be an expert solderer you need four basic ingredients: the right tools, a quick lesson on how to do it, a bit of practice, and enough patience to make a good job of it each and every time. Maybe you are pretty handy with a soldering iron already, or perhaps you have tried once or twice and have given up in frustration. Either way, I hope in a few pages to put you on the right track towards being able to handle any soldering situation you are likely to encounter in the home studio. What's more, I'm not talking about halfway-decent amateur solder jobs. I mean solder joints that will never let you down, up to the limits of the cables and connectors you are joining. Does that sound like a tall order? Well, given the ingredients I have mentioned, with an extra large helping of patience, that is the level of skill anyone can achieve. Let's go to work...

Why solder?

It never does any harm to go right back to basics. What is the point behind soldering? Why is it an appropriate method of making electrical connections?

Touch two bare wires together. You have just made an electrical connection, but is it an adequate connection for audio purposes? Electric current will flow quite happily across a touching connection between two metal surfaces. It will not flow like this for long however. Most metals do not particularly like to exist in their pure form, they have an intrinsic urge to combine with oxygen in the air. Iron, for instance, combines with oxygen to form rust. Oxides of metals are not such good conductors of electricity, so as soon as air gets into a touching connection, conduction will be impaired. Sometimes this can happen in such a way that the joint becomes a crude radio receiver – not a desirable situation in the studio.

What I described above is known as a dry connection. The opposite – a wet connection – happens when a bigger current, large enough actually to weld microscopic areas of the metal surfaces together, flows through the joint. This has more resistance against oxidation, but the currents found in audio circuitry are not really sufficient to 'wet' a joint to any useful

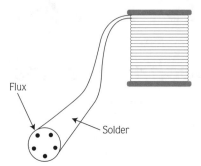

Flux

Solder

Figure 6.1 Multicore solder

extent. We need something to hold the two conductors together, allow current to flow, and keep the air out – solder.

The type of solder used for electrical connections is an alloy of two metals, tin and lead. As you know, the solder is melted and made to flow around the joint. Pretty basic technology, but effective. For our particular needs, the correct type is multicore solder, of which there are several varieties but the most appropriate is 60/40 tin/lead, 18 SWG (Standard Wire Gauge). Figure 6.1 shows a reel with an enlarged view of the cross section.

Left to its own devices, plain tin/lead alloy is not very good for joining metal. It melts easily enough (at about 185 degrees Celsius for a 60/40 alloy) but the resulting liquid does not easily wet the metal surfaces. 'Wet', in this instance, is like water is wet, not as in wet electrical joints. Molten solder will stand in a spherical blob on top of the metal it is meant to adhere to unless it is mixed with a substance known as 'flux'. The flux helps the wetting process and makes the solder flow easily. In multicore solder, the flux is in a number of cores inside the solder wire. In the olden days, flux and solder had to be applied separately. Thank goodness, and technology, we don't have to do that now.

There are other types of solder which are not so good for our purposes. 22 SWG multicore, for example, is great for printed circuit boards, but it is so fine you end up using yards of it for each XLR connector. Another sort known as 'Savbit' (trade name) extends the life of the soldering iron tip, but dries with a dull finish, making it more difficult to tell whether or not you have made a good joint. Other solders may have different melting points. Some are suitable for metals such as aluminium which are difficult to solder, but which are not used in audio circuitry.

Soldering tools

You may have guessed that the first requirement is for a soldering iron. But what type? For the odd connector a 25 watt iron with a tip around 3mm across is suitable, but for heavy duty a temperature controlled 50 watt iron is a must. There are some tiny irons on the market which are not really suitable for soldering audio connectors. They get up to the right temperature, but the tip cools rapidly in use, slowing down the work rate. Sometimes with a small iron, the heat is dissipated in the joint faster than the iron can supply it, resulting in solder that never melts. This generally causes an unwanted rise in the temperature of the operator, through frustration. With a good iron, soldering is easy. It can cost as much as forty or fifty pounds, but the job is made so much more straightforward that it can be considered money well spent.

Essential accessories to the iron are a firm stand and a sponge. The stand will probably have a holder for the sponge, which is used for cleaning the tip. Soldering is one thing, desoldering is quite another, and there is a special tool for the purpose – known as a desoldering tool or solder sucker. This gadget has a spring plunger which, when operated, sucks molten solder from the joint. There always comes a point where solder has to be removed (old solder will have had most of its flux burnt away and will therefore not flow properly). The correct tool is vital. Trying to shift old solder with just an iron is an unrewarding exercise. Also, if you are not blessed with three hands, you will need a vice. A small one will do, or an acceptable alternative is a block of wood with holes drilled to fit the connectors you use. Glue on a male XLR insert so the block will hold female XLRs too. For good soldering, the work piece has to be held firmly. Some people 'get along' without, but why make life more difficult?

To recap, here is a list of the tools that are essential for good results:

50 watt temperature controlled iron with medium (around 3mm) bit
Soldering iron stand
Soldering iron sponge
Vice
Desoldering tool
60/40 tin/lead 18 SWG multicore solder

Possible compromises are a smaller iron (but not too small) and a block of wood as described instead of the vice. Do without a proper stand and you'll risk burning something, possibly yourself.

First steps

The first step once you have unpacked your new iron is to tin the bit. The bit is the removable end piece of the iron, made of copper or iron-coated copper. Tinning the bit simply means applying a coating of solder when the bit is first heated up. I find that the best way is to wrap a coil of solder around the end of the bit while it is cold, switch on and apply more solder as necessary. This protects the bit against oxidation and premature wear.

For your first soldering job, lets try something easy – an XLR connector. Figure 6.2 shows the insert of a male XLR. Have a look at one of your own and you'll see that the ends of the pins where the wire is connected are hollowed out. These hollows are known as 'buckets' or 'solder buckets'. Follow these steps for a perfect joint:

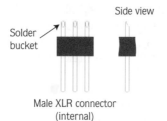

Side view

Solder bucket

Male XLR connector (internal)

Figure 6.2 XLR solder buckets

1 Place the connector shell on a length of mic cable.
2 Remove 20mm of the outer insulation of the cable.
3 Remove 4mm of the insulation on each of the conductors (obviously, the screen conductor is already bare).
4 Clamp the cable lightly in the vice. Twist the end of each conductor.
5 Touch the soldering iron to the bared end of one conductor. At the same time touch the solder to it. The solder will run into the strands of the conductor. Remove iron and solder simultaneously. This procedure is known as 'tinning'. It is absolutely vital that all the strands of the wire are completely covered with solder.
6 Repeat 4 and 5 for the other two conductors. For the screen conductor, just tin 6mm ($^1/_4$ inch) of the end of the bared wire.
7 Place the connector insert in the vice.
8 Touch the soldering iron to one of the buckets, hold for around ten seconds.
9 Keeping the iron on the bucket, melt solder into the bucket until it is nearly full. (Some cheaper XLRs don't have a proper bucket. Make sure there is plenty of solder at the point where the conductor will be attached).
10 Repeat 8 and 9 for the other two buckets.
11 Touch the soldering iron to the bucket of pin 1 (pin numbers are marked on the plastic insert). Hold until the solder melts.
12 Insert the screen conductor into the bucket. Remove the iron and hold still until the solder solidifies.
13 Repeat 11 and 12 for the other two conductors (if the conductors are coloured red and black, connect the red one to pin 2, the black to pin 3).
14 Assemble the connector.

It looks a lot more complicated when it is written down than it is to perform, but if you follow this procedure precisely, then success and a lasting connection will be the result. But what I have described above is the situation when all is going well. At several stages, you need to inspect the cable and connector to make sure that things are as they should be. Here are the possible problems:

1 When the outer insulation is removed, the inner insulation may be damaged. If the inner insulation is cut even slightly or if any of the strands of the screen conductor are cut, start again.
2 When tinning the ends, the insulation may melt. If this happens at any stage of the procedure, start again.
3 When connecting the conductor to the bucket, the solder may not flow freely around the conductor. Unless you see the solder flowing properly at this stage, the joint will not be good. Yes, it has to be done again.
4 If the conductor is moved while the solder is solidifying, the joint will not be good. Often, reapplying the iron and melting the solder already in the bucket will be OK.

The picture is probably becoming clear. You have to see the solder flow like water around the conductor. If you don't, the joint will be bad and will eventually fail. Also, the joint has to be kept rock solid while it cools, or a 'dry joint' will result. A dry joint is one which lets air in, carrying corrosive oxygen. You can often spot a dry joint by its dull finish, but the only sure way to know that a joint is good is to see that the solder flows and solidifies properly as you are making it.

Now is the time to look at the photo showing what it should look like. This is one of mine, and you can see it is fairly tidy. It wasn't achieved with any great amount of skill or dexterity, just practice and patience. And in case you are wondering, I did have to remake one of the joints because it didn't turn out right first time. I removed the old solder, refilled the bucket and retinned the conductor and did it again.

A professional wireman would probably regard this example as a bit on the scruffy side. Wiremen can solder connectors and make them look like jewellery. We ordinary mortals can't expect that level of expertise, but we can make joints that will fulfil their function and, what is most important, will not fail in normal use.

TIPS

*D*on't use the soldering iron to carry blobs of solder to the joint. This technique had its value before multicore solder was invented, but if you do it now, the flux will burn away before it has time to do its work, making the solder flow properly so that it wets the metal surfaces. Don't dab the soldering iron at the joint to try to smooth away any irregularities in the surface of the solder. These irregularities are caused by not heating the joint enough to allow the solder to flow properly. Either melt the solder completely or not at all. Don't try and turn a bad joint into a good one. It can't be done. Use the solder sucker and start again instead.

Figure 6.3 Conductive plastic screened cable soldered to an XLR connector

Making a loom

As I explained earlier, a loom is simply a handy method of making connections in bulk. Between mixer and multitrack, for example.

Materials required

Connectors
Lapped screen cable
Expanding braid sleeve
Heat shrink sleeve
Masking tape
Cable numbers
Heat gun (A hot air paint stripper is a good alternative to a purpose designed heat gun).

The type of connector you use is dictated by the equipment you intend to hook up. The choice of cable is up to you, but it needs to be fairly thin and fairly flexible. Lapped screen is ideal. The first step is to cut it into lengths and make a bundle of all the ends so you can measure the approximate diameter of the loom. You'll need to know this to know what diameter sleeving to order. The expanding braid sleeve is what's going to hold all the cables together throughout the length of the loom. You can see it, and the other items, in the photo. Several diameters are available, but since it expands there will be one to fit your loom exactly. Let's say that your bundle of cables measured 25mm in diameter. Looking in the Electromail catalogue, I see one that expands from 12mm to 30mm. That sounds ideal. The heat shrink sleeve is to hold the expanding sleeve firmly in position at either end. This stuff shrinks to about half its original diameter when heated, so the 38mm size (chosen from the catalogue) seems most suitable to

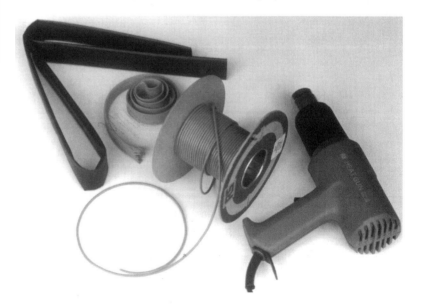

Figure 6.4 Heatshrink sleeving, expanding braid sleeving, lapped screen single conductor cable and hot air gun for making a loom

give a good grip. Let's follow a step-wise procedure once again:

1 Cut the cable into lengths.
2 Number both ends of each length.
3 Solder connectors to one end of each length.
4 Gather together the cables at the connector into a neat bundle. Secure the bundle with masking tape.
5 Arrange the cables into a neat bundle along a length of about 300mm from the last strip of masking tape and secure with more tape (the tape is used to hold the loom together until you can get the sleeve on).
6 Repeat 5 until the entire length is neatly taped up.
7 At the unconnected end, wrap masking tape in a spiral until you have made a point. Don't worry about covering the numbers, this will be removed later.
8 Pass the cables through the expanding sleeve until it reaches the connector end (leaving enough length of cable uncovered so that the connectors can be plugged into the equipment). It's a bit like trying to put a shed skin back on a snake, but you'll get the hang of it.
9 Pass a 100mm length of heat shrink sleeve over the expanding braid towards the connector end until its midpoint is over the end of the braid.
10 Blow hot air over the heat shrink sleeve until it grips firmly.
11 Tighten the braid once more and apply heat shrink sleeve to the other end. Leave enough cable uncovered to suit the connector arrangement on your equipment.
12 Remove excess masking tape.
13 Solder connectors.

Once again, the basic concept is simple, the writing down of it makes it seem more complicated than it is. Figure 6.5 should make the desired result a little more obvious.

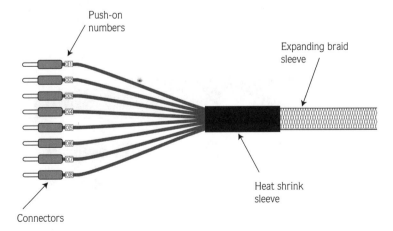

Figure 6.5 One end of the finished cable loom

There are some details which don't fit neatly into a step-wise order. Such as: If you have to cut the expanding braid, it will tend to unravel. The solution is to fuse the loose ends with a soldering iron before it has chance.

So that is how to make a loom. Aside from soldering the connectors, it should take around half an hour. Notice the push-on numbers in Figure 6.5 which of course have to be fitted to both ends of the loom to identify the individual cables, which I make a rule of fixing so that I can hold the end of the cable in my left hand and read them left to right. Without a rule like this, sixes and nines could be mixed up.

Don't forget...

...that the first rule of good soldering and good wiring is never to be satisfied if it's not quite right. Take it apart and do it again. The time spent at this stage will be amply repaid later on. Problems during recording sessions due to faulty soldering are entirely unnecessary. Problems due to poor connector design are another matter, but if you buy your connectors from a reliable source (usually not the local electrical shop where you buy your replacement kettle elements) these problems can be minimised.

Soldering phono connectors

It's always best to get good quality phonos, the cheapest sort really are just not worth the bother. One acceptable type is shown in Figure 6.6b. Between the diagram and the photo you should get a good idea of how to

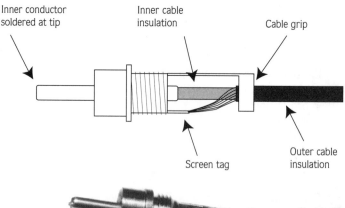

Figure 6.6a Phono connector

Figure 6.6b Lapped screen cable prepared for, and soldered to, a phono connector

solder a phono connector. The first step is to prepare the cable as in the photo, with a long tinned inner conductor. This conductor should be threaded through the connector until it appears through the hole in the tip, where it is soldered. Snip off any excess wire. Also, the outer insulation should come about a millimetre inside the cable clamp, which should be pinched firmly with a pair of pliers before soldering the screen.

There is a distinct risk in most designs of phono that the screen could come in contact with the inner conductor – either as it is soldered, or later in use. To avoid this, bend the screen backwards and away from the centre of the connector before soldering it to the tag. If it comes closer than a millimetre to the central pin, it will create a short sooner or later in service.

7

Patchbays

Dashing through the undergrowth, one false move and your foot becomes entangled in a wire noose. The trap is sprung and the tree branch snaps upwards, leaving you dangling upside down and helpless beneath it. Is this a scene from the latest action movie, or a typical day in the studio? There must be a more practical way...

I have a crusade against cables. I hate them. But a typical home or project studio can contain several hundred metres of cabling, a professional studio may have miles – literally. But there are ways to keep the cables out of the work space and get them into a sensible arrangement where they will do most good, and cause you the least amount of inconvenience. At the heart of a good cabling system there is the patchbay – or jackfield if you prefer old-fashioned, un-Americanised English. The patchbay is simply a device to place all the equipment connections within easy reach, and in a logical format. There is no need to grovel about in dark corners plugging in equipment. Nor is there need to keep a multitude of adaptor cables, phono to XLR, XLR to jack, jack back to phono again.

Let's get down to the basics...

Why have a patchbay?

You will not be unaware that every piece of audio or electronic musical gear you own has an extensive array of connectors at the back. Neither will you be unaware that to make a studio work, all these items of equipment have to be connected together. That's the starting point. But how do you go about making all these connections in a sensible manner? The usual way most people start in home recording is to have just a small amount of gear and they use cables to go directly from one piece of equipment to another. Let's say you have a 4-track cassette deck, add to that a synthesiser, a stereo tape recorder, monitor amp and speakers. At the very least, this amounts to five line-level cables, possibly:

1 x jack to jack (synth to 4-track)
2 x phono to phono (4-track to stereo tape)
2 x phono to XLR (stereo tape to monitor amp)

Already this is a fine assortment of different connector and cable types. As the set-up increases in size and complexity, the assortment grows.

Eventually you find yourself in an immense tangle of leads every time you want to reconfigure your equipment, or perhaps want to do something special for a musical effect. With a patchbay – even a very rudimentary one – connection and reconnection become a lot easier. Now, all the inputs and outputs of the various pieces of equipment are wired to rows of jack sockets, all on one panel. Standard cables with identical connectors – called patchcords – can be used to connect the system together in any way you wish. No fuss, no bother. Let's now progress to a very simple practical example. I'll stick to the cassette 4-track, one synth, stereo cassette deck for mastering, amp and speakers, and add to it an effects unit, possibly a reverb. The first step in patchbay implementation is to make a list of equipment connections. Like this:

4-track	4 inputs (jack)	1 aux (effect) output (phono)	2 aux inputs (phono)	2 main outputs (phono)	2 monitor outputs (phono)
Synth	1 output (jack)				
Effects unit	1 input (jack)	2 outputs (jack)			
Stereo cassette	2 inputs (phono)	2 outputs (phono)			
Monitor amp	2 inputs (phono)				

Two things to note. First, this is the very simplest system I can think of, without becoming too trivial – that's why the synth has only one output! But still, this will be a good example. Second, that speaker wiring has no place in the patchbay system. There are such things as loudspeaker patchbays, but they bear the same relationship to the home studio as a Challenger tank does to a Fiat Punto.

Figure 7.1 shows how the system would be connected without using a patchbay. To make connections via a patchbay, we first need to design a sensible patchbay layout.

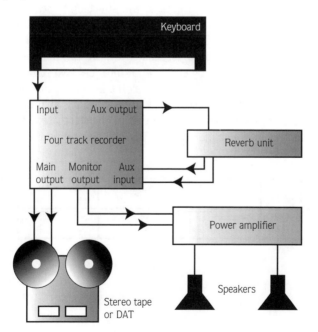

Figure 7.1 Simple studio setup without patchbay

Figure 7.2 shows a schematic, and the flow of the signal from source to final stereo mix and speakers. This isn't how it will finally look but we need to take a careful step-by-step approach at this stage. As you might have noticed, each row is either all outputs or all inputs. Output rows and input rows alternate all the way down. The primary signal source is the synth, therefore its output is on the top row. Directly below it is the input of the 4-track to which it will normally be connected – input 1.

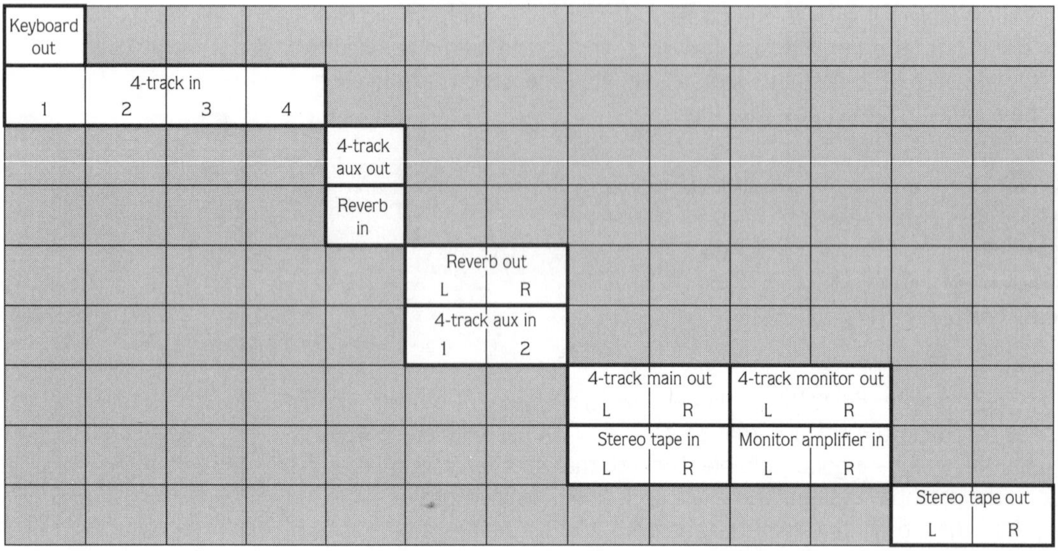

Keyboard out												
1	4-track in 2	3	4									
				4-track aux out								
				Reverb in								
					Reverb out L	R						
					4-track aux in 1	2						
							4-track main out L	R	4-track monitor out L	R		
							Stereo tape in L	R	Monitor amplifier in L	R		
											Stereo tape out L	R

Figure 7.2 'Expanded' patchbay layout

Next in the signal chain is the 4-track's auxiliary (effect) output. Directly below that is the effect unit's input. And so on. In the next row of outputs appear the outputs of the effect unit. Beneath them are the 4-track's auxiliary inputs. Get the picture? Rows of outputs and inputs always alternate. Outputs and inputs which will normally be connected together are paired up vertically. Now we can make the diagram simpler and more practical by shrinking it into just two rows. Row 1 has all the equipment outputs. Row 2 has all the inputs, as in Figure 7.3. The entire system could be hooked up with just eight patchcords. When the final stereo mix is complete, the output of the stereo tape can be patched in to the monitor amplifier for auditioning (as long as the monitor amp has a volume control).

Figure 7.3 The finished patchbay layout

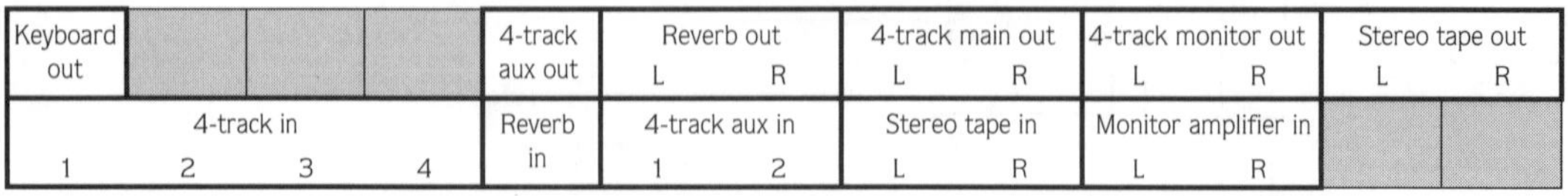

Keyboard out				4-track aux out	Reverb out L	R	4-track main out L	R	4-track monitor out L	R	Stereo tape out L	R
1	4-track in 2	3	4	Reverb in	4-track aux in 1	2	Stereo tape in L	R	Monitor amplifier in L	R		

The real world

Now that we have the basic theory, it's time to look in more detail at a real patchbay. And why not go straight to the top – to a professional quality patchbay of the kind used by recording studios, radio and TV stations, the world over. My own patchbay is shown in Figure 7.4. It may look complicated, but it is just a grown up example of what I have described above. The principle is no different, and once you understand them, patchbays really do make your life much easier.

Figure 7.4 The author's patchbay

A typical patchbay unit comes as a 3U rack-mounting panel containing three rows of 24 jacks, totalling 48 connections. Some types have more rows, others have different numbers of jacks in each row. Figure 7.5 shows the overall construction. Figure 7.6 shows the configuration of the individual jack sockets.

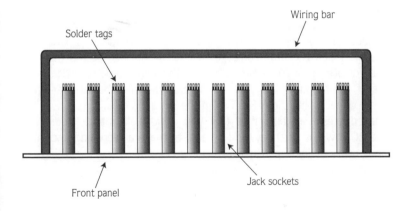

Wiring bar

Solder tags

Jack sockets

Front panel

Figure 7.5 Patchbay construction

The jack socket, of the type conventionally employed, has five tags to which wires may be soldered. It seems like two too many, so what can they all be for? Obviously, three of the tags must be for the balanced audio cable (two signal conductors plus screen). The other two tags go to

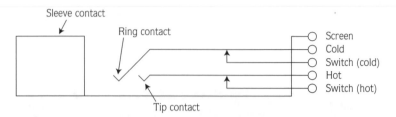

Figure 7.6 Type B jack socket

switch contacts in the body of the socket. These switch contacts press against the two signal contacts when the socket does not have a jack plug inserted. But they are forced apart when the plug is placed in position. The switch contacts can be used to connect equipment together, using an important technique known as normalling.

Normalling

Going back to the simple example outlined earlier, you can see that the patchbay was designed to suit the normal way the equipment will be connected together. For every studio, there is a configuration of equipment that will be good for 90% of the tasks undertaken. Using the normalling technique, the patchbay can be used to make all these connections, through the switch contacts of the jacks, without any patchcords being plugged in, by the attachment of wire links at the rear of the panel. If the engineer wants to do something out of the ordinary, and reconfigure the connections between the equipment, all he or she has to do is to overplug the normals – which means that when patchcords are inserted to make new connections, the switch contacts of the jacks are forced apart and the old connections are temporarily broken.

In the simple example, normalling can be used to make all the connections necessary for the track laying and mixing procedure. No patchcords necessary. When the time comes to check the finished stereo mix, two patchcords are taken from the outputs of the stereo tape recorder to the inputs of the monitor amp. The act of plugging into the monitor amp's jacks disconnects the original link from the 4-track's main outputs.

The end result of all this is that you could walk into a studio with maybe 20 rows of patchbay, and be able to make a recording and mix it without using a single patchcord. But if you want to try something creative, all you do is make the new patch you want and the original connection will be unmade automatically.

The type B jack connector

Type B jacks were once known as 'GPO jacks' because they were used in old-style telephone switchboards. They, or the smaller but similar bantam jack, are still in use today in just about every studio with a patchbay. A typical type B jack is made of brass with a plastic sleeve and looks something like the standard ¼ inch jack that is used in musical and home recording equipment. Although the type B is the same diameter and length, the tip is smaller, so it is best not to mix the two types. If a type B jack plug is plugged into a standard jack (type A) socket, then it may not make proper contact. If a standard jack plug is forced into a type B socket, it will work but may damage the contacts.

The type B jack socket has a brass frame, and five contacts (two signal contacts for balanced lines, plus screen). The signal contacts each have a normally-closed switch contact, which disconnects when a jack plug is inserted. Other contact arrangements are made for special purposes, but this is the most common. In a patchbay, the type B sockets are arranged in horizontal rows, 16 to 26 jacks across. Obviously, the more jacks in a row, the greater the packing density. Often patchbays come as one row of jacks per 1U of rack space. Some types are more compressed and fit two rows into the same space. It should be remembered that the higher the density of the patchbay, the more soldering expertise it will demand.

To help secure the incoming cables, of which there will be many, there is a wiring bar for each of the rows of jacks. Each cable is fixed to this bar as it leaves the jack, forming a neat bundle passing all the way to one end of the patchbay, as you can see in Figure 7.7.

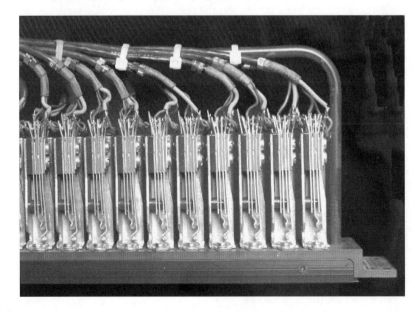

Figure 7.7 Inside the patchbay

Expert patchbay layout

The possession of a patchbay marks the difference between a conglomeration of miscellaneous equipment and a versatile working studio. Every home or project studio is different, as is every home or project studio owner. We all have our little quirks and idiosyncrasies and it reflects in the way we like to organise our gear and make music. And that gives the home studio a big advantage over the otherwise well specified commercial studio. Anyone hiring a commercial studio has to accept someone else's ideas on how a studio should be organised, and work within whatever restrictions the system imposes. But with your own personal studio set-up – it's all up to you. You might not have as much gear, but it can be put together in a way that works well for you.

For any recording set up, there is an optimum way of hooking all the equipment together. In fact, there may be an almost infinite number of usable hook-ups with even a small amount of gear. But there will be one arrangement which will suit most of your requirements, most of the time. The principal justification for having a patchbay is the added flexibility it affords. Let's calculate the benefits:

Suppose a rich aunt gave you £5000 for some equipment. You had it delivered, and connected everything together point-to-point, input-to-output with no patchbay, in the way you decided would suit your needs 75% of the time. The chances are that you would not be inclined to do much replugging of connections during sessions, because they are all out of the way round the back of the equipment, and they are such an assortment of different connector types. The patchbay lets you have the system you want 100% of the time, by making the connections instantly available. So if your equipment cost £5000, that extra 25% represents some £1600 worth of value. It isn't often you get something for nothing in this world, but for a modest outlay on a patchbay, you are getting a much greater return in terms of the added potential of your equipment.

Patchbay planning

When your patchbay is delivered, hotfoot from one of the studio suppliers, it is like a blank sheet of paper – or blank reel of tape if you prefer. It's up to you to decide how your equipment is going to be connected to it. But that's not so hard once you have the idea. For the purpose of this example I have dreamed up a 16-track system, with a few instruments and effects units. What I need to work out is to which sockets on the patchbay all the inputs and outputs of the equipment should be connected to make things neat, and to offer the versatility I require. The equipment, together with its connections is listed in the table on page 64. Figure 7.8 (a) shows the system connected point to point, and Figure 7.8 (b) shows it connected via the patchbay.

It's not a big system, and perhaps a little oversimplified, but it's enough for the purpose of this example. As you can see, every connection on each piece of equipment is made via the patchbay, with just a couple of

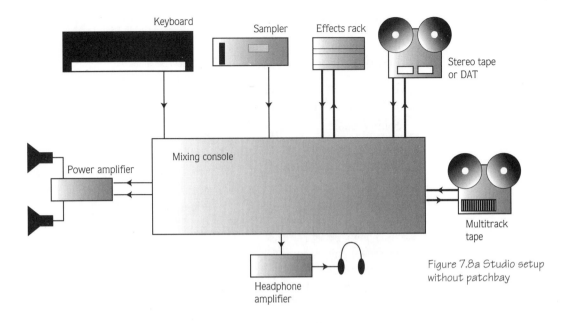

Figure 7.8a Studio setup without patchbay

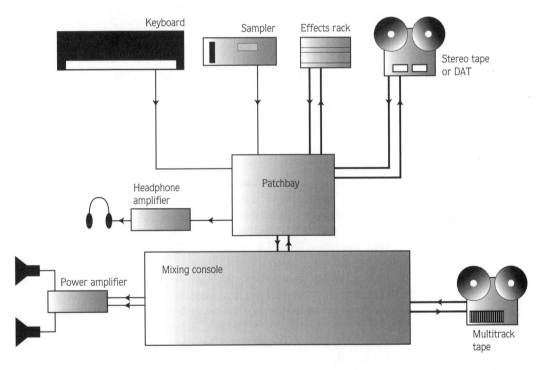

Figure 7.8b Studio setup with patchbay

exceptions. Usually, there is not that much to be gained by having the connections to the multitrack, and the corresponding mixing console connections, on the patchbay. It would be a rare situation where you needed to repatch these. On the other hand, if you want to include these you may well find a use for the extra flexibility.

Equipment connections

Instruments		*Stereo recorder*	
		2 inputs	
Sampler	8 outputs	2 outputs	
Keyboard	2 outputs		
Synth module 1	2 outputs	*Compressor/limiter*	
Synth module 2	2 outputs	2 inputs	
		2 outputs	
Recording equipment		2 side chain inputs	
Mixing console		*Noise gate*	
16 line inputs		2 inputs	
16 channel insert sends		2 outputs	
16 channel insert returns		2 external key inputs	
16 tape monitor inputs*			
8 group outputs*		*Reverb unit 1*	
8 group insert sends		1 input	
8 group insert returns		2 outputs	
4 auxiliary sends			
4 auxiliary inputs		*Reverb unit 2*	
2 master outputs		1 input	
2 monitor outputs*		2 outputs	
2 stereo returns			
		Multieffects unit	
Multitrack recorder		1 input	
16 inputs*		2 outputs	
16 outputs*			
		Power amplifier	
		2 inputs*	

* In this example, the marked connections do not appear on the patchbay.

The next job is to count them all up. I make it 115 connections. This means that we shall need at least 115 sockets on our patchbay. Add a few for expansion and a few for luck, and 160 becomes a reasonable estimate. Now we have to decide what the normal state of the studio will be – how the connections should made so that the system is correctly wired for normal day-to-day use.

When the patchbay is wired up, it will be usable without employing any patchcords. But any changes you need to make will be done by simply 'overplugging' the patchbay. The process of wiring the patchbay so that patchcords are, for most of the time, unnecessary is called normalling (or normalising) and I shall describe the method of actually wiring a normal in detail shortly.

Normal connections

From	To
Sampler outputs 1 – 8	Line inputs 1 – 8
Keyboard outputs 1 – 2	Line inputs 9 – 10
Synth module 1 outputs 1 – 2	Line inputs 11 – 12
Synth module 2 outputs 1 – 2	Line inputs 13 – 14
Multieffects unit outputs 1 – 2	Line input 15 – 16
Auxiliary send 1	Foldback amplifier input
Auxiliary send 2	Multieffects unit input
Auxiliary send 3	Reverb unit 1 input
Auxiliary send 4	Reverb unit 2 input
Channel insert sends 1 – 16	Channel insert returns 1 – 16
Reverb unit 1 output L	Auxiliary input 1
Reverb unit 1 output R	Auxiliary input 2
Reverb unit 2 output L	Auxiliary input 3
Reverb unit 2 output R	Auxiliary input 4
Group insert sends 1 – 8	Group insert returns 1 – 8
Master output L	Stereo recorder input L
Master output R	Stereo recorder input R
Stereo recorder output L	2T monitor L
Stereo recorder output R	2T monitor R

Usually, to arrange for normal connections in the patchbay you have to make sure that outputs are vertically above the inputs to which they will be normalled. In fact, it is best to have complete alternate rows of outputs and inputs. This makes things easy to organise and to arrange. The next task is to draw a diagram of the patchbay layout. I like to do this on A3 size graph paper. I draw a grid with the appropriate number of boxes across, representing the sockets, and whatever number of rows down to make up the right quantity of connections. In this case, I have chosen to use eight rows of patchbay, each twenty sockets across (Figure 7.9). With a bit of juggling, everything can be made to fit in a logical order, accord-

Figure 7.9 Full patchbay layout

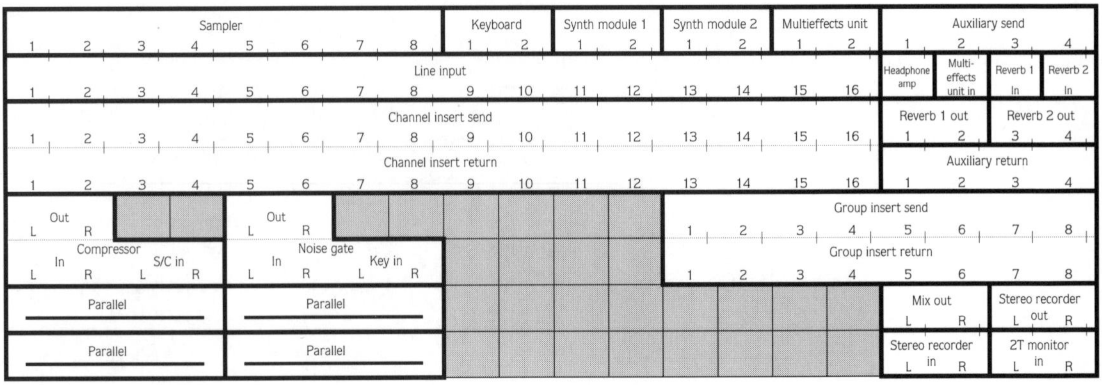

Sampler								Keyboard		Synth module 1		Synth module 2		Multieffects unit		Auxiliary send			
1	2	3	4	5	6	7	8	1	2	1	2	1	2	1	2	1	2	3	4
Line input																Headphone amp	Multieffects unit in	Reverb 1 In	Reverb 2 In
1	2	3	4	5	6	7	8	9	10	11	12	13	14	15	16				
Channel insert send																Reverb 1 out		Reverb 2 out	
1	2	3	4	5	6	7	8	9	10	11	12	13	14	15	16	1	2	3	4
Channel insert return																Auxiliary return			
1	2	3	4	5	6	7	8	9	10	11	12	13	14	15	16	1	2	3	4
Out				Out								Group insert send							
L	R			L	R							1	2	3	4	5	6	7	8
Compressor				Noise gate								Group insert return							
In		S/C in		In		Key in													
L	R	L	R	L	R	L	R					1	2	3	4	5	6	7	8
Parallel				Parallel												Mix out		Stereo recorder out	
																L	R	L	R
Parallel				Parallel												Stereo recorder in		2T monitor in	
																L	R	L	R

ing to the two lists drawn up previously. Normals are indicated by a short line joining upper and lower sockets.

With the layout diagram complete, you can make a third list ('Patchbay Wiring Schedule' shows two rows) detailing patchbay row/socket, connection and type of connector. It may seem like a chore to have to do all this paperwork, but proper planning will result in trouble-free wiring – and no annoying mistakes. In Figure 7.9 several sockets are unallocated. It is better to have unallocated sockets than to squeeze everything into a cluttered layout. As you buy more equipment, these extra sockets will be taken up.

Here I have also allowed for four sets of paralleled sockets. These are simply sockets with their signal and earth connections wired across. They are used to split outputs to two or three destinations.

Patchbay wiring schedule

Row/socket	Connection	Connector
1/01	Sampler output 1	jack
1/02	Sampler output 2	jack
1/03	Sampler output 3	jack
1/04	Sampler output 4	jack
1/05	Sampler output 5	jack
1/06	Sampler output 6	jack
1/07	Sampler output 7	jack
1/08	Sampler output 8	jack
1/09	Keyboard output 1	jack
1/10	Keyboard output 2	jack
1/11	Synth module 1 output 1	jack
1/12	Synth module 1 output 2	jack
1/13	Synth module 2 output 1	jack
1/14	Synth module 2 output 2	jack
1/15	Multieffects output 1	jack
1/16	Multieffects output 2	jack
1/17	Auxiliary send 1	jack
1/18	Auxiliary send 2	jack
1/19	Auxiliary send 3	jack
1/20	Auxiliary send 4	jack
2/01	Line input 1	stereo jack *
2/02	Line input 2	stereo jack
2/03	Line input 3	stereo jack
2/04	Line input 4	stereo jack
2/05	Line input 5	stereo jack
2/06	Line input 6	stereo jack
2/07	Line input 7	stereo jack
2/08	Line input 8	stereo jack
2/09	Line input 9	stereo jack
2/10	Line input 10	stereo jack

2/11	Line input 11	stereo jack
2/12	Line input 12	stereo jack
2/13	Line input 13	stereo jack
2/14	Line input 14	stereo jack
2/15	Line input 15	stereo jack
2/16	Line input 16	stereo jack
2/17	Headphone amp input	XLR (male)
2/18	Multieffects input	jack
2/19	Reverb unit 1 input	jack
2/20	Reverb unit 2 input	jack

* Note that mixer inputs often use a stereo jack to provide a balanced input. Other types of equipment, and mixer outputs, normally use a mono jack.

Wiring the patchbay

When the planning process is complete, then it's time to start the action. You can do it all on the workbench, making sure that the mixer cables will be long enough for your intended studio layout (you could make them into a loom, as described in Chapter 6), and that the rack equipment cables are long enough to go anywhere in the rack. After all, you don't know how you may want to rearrange things in the future. You could even cable up the unallocated sockets on the jackfield, ready to plug in the new equipment that you will undoubtedly buy as your home or project studio venture succeeds. Don't forget that each cable will need to be numbered at both ends, with the push-on cables numbers specifically made for the purpose. And how do you work out the number for each cable? Why, it's the same as the patchbay row/socket number – you have done that job already.

Patchbay wiring is probably the most difficult type of wiring you will ever do in your studio. When I described how to solder connectors in Chapter 6, I said that anyone can do it. I'm not sure that the same can be said here. A lot of practice, or a natural gift of neatness, is essential before starting something like this. But if you are sure that your soldering is up to it, here is how to wire a patchbay:

Let's assume that you are using balanced cables, of the foil screened twin sort described in Chapter 5. You will need some extra tools and materials to add to what you probably already have:

Binding sleeves size
H20 sleeving tool (dilator)
Sleeve lubricant
Green silicone rubber sleeving (1mm bore diameter)
7/.02 cable – in red, black and green

Not such a lot, but essential. Assuming the design of the patchbay is complete, you should first set about putting the wiring for the normals in place. This is done using the 7/.02 cable. ('7/.02', by the way, means that the wire has seven copper strands each .02mm in diameter). For each normal you intend to make, cut off a three inch (75mm) length of each of the three colours and twist them together. Then strip and tin the ends. These will be soldered to the hot, cold and screen contacts of the upper (output) jack, and to the switch (hot), switch (cold) and screen contacts of the lower (input) jack for a half normal. Remember that red = hot, black = cold, green = screen.

Solder each wire to the appropriate tag on the upper jack, making sure to push the wires through the hole in each tag and wrap them once around the metal. This will help keep them in place when you solder the signal cables onto the same tags. Take a look at Figure 7.10 to check your connections so far.

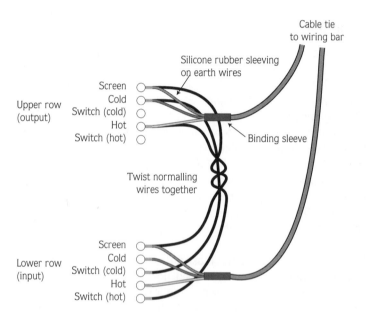

Figure 7.10 Half normal wiring

Next, solder the other ends of the normalling wire to the appropriate tags on the lower connector. This time don't wrap the red and black signal conductors around the holes. A good solder joint will be strong enough without this mechanical attachment and corrections/modifications will be easier. Hopefully, the normalling will be nice and neat, and still leave room for the signal cables to get in. It's best to push the normalling wiring down between the jacks where it doesn't get in the way.

When you have finished all the normals you need, it's time for the signal cables. I'll deal with just one individual signal cable, otherwise it could get complex. Assuming it's the right cable and it's in the right place, then you need to carry out the following steps, as shown in Figure 7.11.

1 Strip the outer insulation to about 30mm.
2 Strip the red and black (signal) conductors to 5mm.
3 Cut off a length of green sleeving and place it on the bare screen conductor, leaving 5mm of bare wire showing.
4 Place an H20 binding sleeve on the lubricated tips of the sleeving tool.
5 Expand the tool and position the sleeve over the end of the outer insulation of the cable to hold the whole lot together

Now that you have a nice neat end to the cable, solder the red conductor to the hot tag (as seen in Figure 7.10), the black conductor to the cold tag, and the green screen to the – guess what – the screen tag. The photo sequence should help put all the above into the correct perspective. I would like to say that it isn't difficult, but that would give a false impression. It can be very fiddly to wire a patchbay, but it can be done with patience and the correct application of hard work.

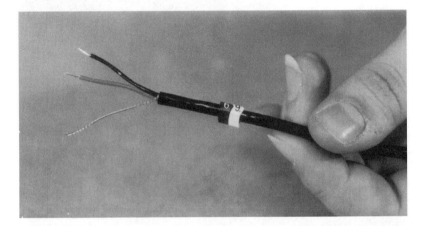

Figure 7.11a Stripped FST cable

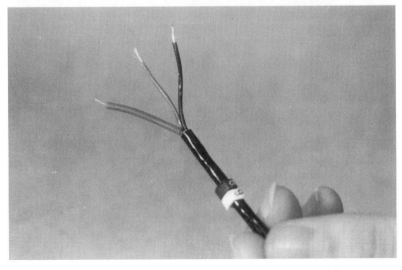

Figure 7.11b Silicone rubber sleeving placed over the screen conductor

Figure 7.11c Lubricating the sleeving tool

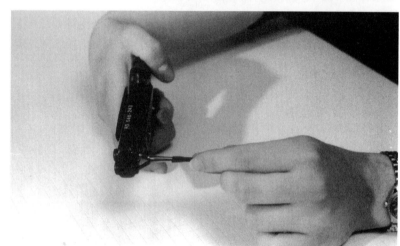

Figure 7.11d Placing a binding sleeve on the sleeving tool

Figure 7.11e Positioning the binding sleeve on the cable

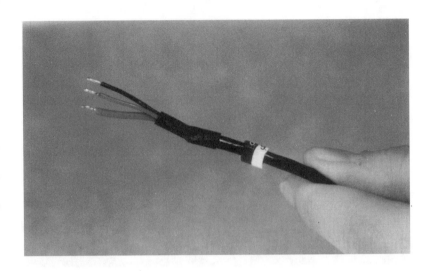

Figure 7.11f The finished cable

Easy patchbay wiring

I have written at some length on the subject of patchbays because I consider them important – and so does just about every studio in existence. Without a patchbay, an engineer is continually struggling with cables and connectors. With a well designed patchbay, all the inputs and outputs of the studio equipment are instantly available for any possible creative connection. The type B jack patchbays (or their miniature equivalent, the Bantam jack), as used by pro studios, are efficient and reliable. Unfortunately, they are also expensive and difficult to wire up. But there is a cheaper way, very suitable for the home studio owner. Type A jack connectors (ordinary everyday jacks) are almost as good as the more expensive type B jack connector. In fact, practically the only reason why they are less well respected is that there have been so many rogue manufacturers making poor quality versions.

Well designed type A jacks can give a very reliable connection. Isotrack is just one company offering a range of patchbay systems based on the type A jack, which they call their Signex patchbay systems. They are not only much cheaper than type B patchbays, they are much easier to install.

Connection of equipment to the patchbay is easy too, with options. Unlike the normalling options which are user configured, the connection option must be specified at the time of order. Perhaps the most simple way to connect your equipment to the patchbay is via rear-mounted 1/4 inch jacks. You could possibly avoid soldering altogether! Or you can have

INFORMATION

The Signex CP44 is a 44-way patchbay unit with a variety of options. The system is based on a printed circuit board (PCB) to which each vertical pair of jacks is mounted. The printed circuit board offers a variety of normalling options. You can configure the board as half-normal, full-normal or unnormalled. Soldering expertise is not required in any great abundance because to select any of the options all you have to do is to bridge two pads on the printed circuit with a blob of solder. As long as you avoid the dreaded dry joint all will be neat and perfect.

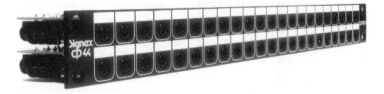

Figure 7.12a The Signex CP44 offers a variety of options

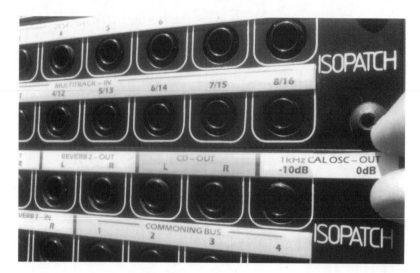

Figure 7.12b Fitting a designation strip to an Isopatch patchbay to identify the connections

phonos or simply solder straight onto the PCB. All the PCBs are demountable so you shouldn't have any trouble.

Half and full normals

Normalling simply means that all normal studio interconnections can be made using the switch contacts of the patchbay jack sockets, without using patchcords. Each socket has two solder tags for the jack contacts plus one for the screen, and two for the switch contacts. Wiring between output and input jacks is shown in Figure 7.13. This is known as a 'half normal'. A patchcord may be plugged into an output socket and used as a parallel connection and the output of the equipment may be split in two

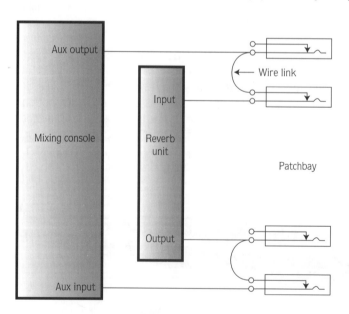

Figure 7.13 Simplified diagram of a half normal

destinations. But when a patchcord is plugged into an input socket it over-rides ('overplugs') the existing switch connection. This is the normalling method most commonly used in studios.

A 'full normal' (Figure 7.14) is made by slightly modifying the connections to the output jack. When a patchcord is plugged into either the output or the input, it breaks away the normal connection. Full normals are not in common use in recording studios, but I don't think it will harm you to have heard of them.

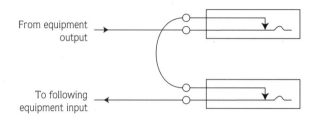

Figure 7.14 Detail of full normal

Earth loops

With unbalanced equipment, i.e. normal semi-pro gear, there is the possibility of an earth loop occurring because of the mains wiring arrangements which will create an annoying hum in your speakers and on your recordings. Ideally, the entire system should be earthed at only one point and if more than one piece of equipment is connected via its own mains lead to earth, then an earth loop will be created through the screen of the signal connection cable.

A common cure for this is to disconnect the earth wires of all but one piece of equipment in the set up. The equipment will still be earthed, but through the screens of the signal cables. Unfortunately, although this will cure the earth loop and get rid of the hum, it isn't safe because it would be very easy to remove an item of equipment from the setup and use it without an earth. The most practical alternative is not to connect the screen of the cable at the input(s) of any piece of equipment which has an earth in its mains lead. Where equipment is designed not to have a mains earth, then the screen must be connected.

8

Advanced interconnection

While it's not necessary for the studio builder to understand the more esoteric aspects of cables, the following sections will be of use to those really wanting to get to grips with the subject.

To state the obvious, the purpose of an electrical cable is to carry signals from one end to the other without either gaining or losing anything. What comes out should be what went in, in other words. In an imperfect world this can never happen, but there are methods to minimise the problems that occur. What we might gain in the cable is interference. This could be clicks generated by refrigerators, thermostats etc elsewhere in the building (or even the building next door), or hum – which lurks anywhere there is AC mains nearby. Worst of all is dimmer noise from lighting control units. Theatre and PA sound engineers know all about this little nasty, which can work its way into the most professional of set-ups.

There are two ways clicks and buzzes can get into your system, through the air and through the mains wiring. Mains borne interference can normally be dealt with using filters which plug between your equipment and the wall socket. They vary in price and capabilities from cheap and cheerful, to medical standard – which will prevent your heart and lung machine from giving up the ghost on your behalf! You will need to have a good mains earth however, which is more your local electrician's province than mine so consult him if you have any doubts. You might be doing yourself a favour in more ways than one.

Airborne interference is the main topic here because this is how gremlins can get into your music via the audio cabling. We all know how radio waves can travel through the air from the transmitter to your portable radio, and interference works in exactly the same way. Electromagnetic radiation (of which radio waves are just one kind) is created anywhere there is an electric field. The problem areas as far as we are concerned being wiring between equipment and the mains supply – which can cause hum – and switching sparks which induce crackling noises into the audio cables.

Copper wire, or any sort of conducting wire, is heaven for electromagnetic interference. The attraction is of the dog-to-lamp post order and an efficient solution in either case would be some form of fence to protect our nice clean signal (or lamp post) from being sullied. This is done, as in Figure 8.1, by wrapping a screen of copper wire around the signal

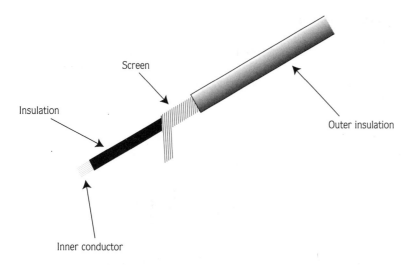

Figure 8.1 Screened single conductor cable

carrying conductor. Interference gets into the screen and is conducted harmlessly away to earth, or at least most of it is. This is a simple and largely effective system, and has the advantage that the screen can be used as part of the audio signal circuit and indeed is in most domestic and semi-professional audio equipment.

The disadvantage of using the screen as part of the audio circuit is that it can act as an open door to hum. All you need is to connect the screens together in a continuous loop and then connect to mains earth in two or more places. This is the infamous earth loop situation. Any audio installation which uses the screen as part of the signal circuit and is connected to mains earth at more than one point will hum like crazy (Figure 8.2). I shall explain how to get round the problem later but in the meantime, don't go disconnecting any earth connections on your equipment or I might find myself with a lawsuit for encouraging death by electrocution. I might write in a light-hearted manner but this point is serious. Never use equipment with the mains earth disconnected. Musicians have done this and not lived to tell the tale.

Losses in the cable are caused by signal 'leaking' between conductor and screen. If you use cheap cable than this is what you can expect. These losses are explained more fully in Chapter 5.

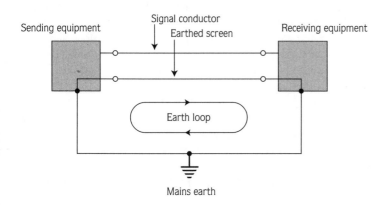

Figure 8.2 Earth loop

Balanced and unbalanced

The system which I have just discussed, and with which you are probably most familiar, is the unbalanced system of interconnection. The balanced system, which is normally used in fully professional equipment, uses an extra signal conductor – so removing the need to use the screen as part of the signal carrying circuit. Figure 8.3 explains.

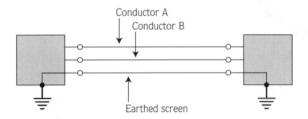

Figure 8.3 Balanced connection between equipment

The word 'balanced' really means 'equal and opposite'. The signal on one conductor is balanced by an equal and opposite signal on the other conductor. Equal in strength but opposite in polarity. The balanced signal – say from the balanced output of a microphone – travels down the cable to the balanced input of the mixer, where the difference between the voltages on the two conductors is measured and passed on to the rest of the circuitry. A mathematical explanation is given later. The clever part of all this is that any interference which gets through the screen affects each conductor equally. As the balanced input stage responds only to differences in voltages in the conductors, the interference is rejected. Earth loops are also thrown out of the window because the circuitry at either end of the cable pays absolutely no attention to what is going on electrically in the screen, as long as it is connected to earth.

There is a technical term for the amount of interference suppression a balanced input stage gives, called the Common Mode Rejection Ratio which is measured in decibels. 60dB would be a good figure for a microphone input and should cover most eventualities.

Balanced meets unbalanced

So far, we have discussed balanced systems and unbalanced systems. In the real world we are going to have to use them both together and it gets a bit complicated. A few diagrams and a few words of explanation will cover most combinations. I shall start with the simple situations and work up from there.

Unbalanced to unbalanced

This is the normal semi-pro and domestic system. As I said earlier, there must be only one connection to earth in the system or you will get mains hum. There are two ways of doing this which I am afraid are both unsatisfactory in certain respects. One is potentially unsafe and the other is a bit fiddly. Oh well...

Figure 8.4a can represent any number of pieces of equipment. As you

(a)

(b)

Screen broken here

Figure 8.4 Unbalanced to unbalanced

can see, both conductor and screen are connected at both ends but only one item of equipment is connected to mains earth. Some engineers will disconnect the earth to all but one of the items which will definitely get rid of the earth loop, and the earth will still be connected around the whole system via the screens of the cables. The problem here is that if you are in the habit of moving gear around, setting it up and taking it down, there is the risk that you will plug in and switch on something that has not yet been connected to earth via the screen of the signal cable. If the equipment is faulty you could be in for a shock – literally. Murphy's law will eventually apply and someone will suffer as a result, so even though it does cure an earth loop, removing a mains earth can't be recommended. You may have noticed that some of your equipment needs no mains earth. This is because it is constructed in a way that gives a high degree of mains safety and passes the relevant safety standard.

Figure 8.4b shows a different way. The screen of each connecting cable is attached at one end only. Each individual item can then have its own mains earth and the screen still fulfils its protective function. The safety advantages are obvious but you end up with some cables with their screens snipped, some without. If you use a cable with its screen snipped to connect one piece of equipment with a mains earth to a piece of equipment that doesn't need one, it won't work, and you'll probably be left wondering why.

Balanced to balanced
No problems. Plug it in and away you go. The pros use this system because they don't have to think about what they are doing!

Unbalanced to balanced
In other words, one conductor and a screen from the sending equipment have to be connected to two conductors and a screen at the receiving end. There are two ways of doing this. Figure 8.5a shows the usual method

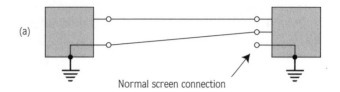

(a)

Normal screen connection

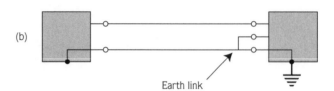

(b)

Earth link

Figure 8.5 Unbalanced to balanced

for mains powered (and earthed) equipment. Figure 8.5b shows how to connect an unearthed item like a microphone or synthesiser without a mains earth connection. In either case, get it the wrong way round and you will get hum. It's a hard life.

Balanced to unbalanced

Balanced gear often uses transformers to convert one-conductor signals to two-conductor signals and vice-versa. Transformers are simple in practice and they work well enough. Unfortunately, a line output transformer costs around £20 and can weigh up to a kilogram. I don't have to say why some manufacturers use other methods of balancing do I? Electronic balancing is the other method, often superior to transformer balancing and very cheap, but there is a problem.

Look at Figure 8.6a. This is how to unbalance a transformer output by connecting one signal conductor to earth. Many electronically balanced outputs will not allow you to do this so you must use Figure 8.6b. Some clever manufacturers have an electronically balanced output that mimics a

(a)

Link to screen

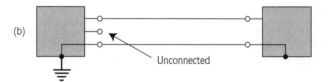

(b)

Unconnected

Figure 8.6 Balanced to unbalanced

transformer so you must use 8.6a. It's a minefield! The only answer is to consult the manual and don't forget that that we are back in earth loop territory again.

If your system is mostly balanced it is usually best to make any balanced-to-unbalanced adjustments at the connector nearest the item of equipment you want to adapt to your standard. If you are unbalanced and are using single conductor cable then you will not have this choice to make.

These diagrams will see you through most of the situations you will encounter with professional and semi-professional equipment. If you intend to work at the very highest level, you will find that earthing is taken an order of magnitude more seriously, with separate earthing for the chassis (and motors etc) of the equipment and the audio signals. In a small installation, you don't need to do this. The diagrams adequately deal with every problem I have encountered in my home studio.

Mathematical description of balanced line operation.

Let the signal voltages on the conductors be $+V$ and $-V$. Call the interference voltage on each conductor X.

Voltage on conductor A; $+V + X$
Voltage on conductor B; $-V + X$

The balanced input stage responds to the difference:

$$+V + X - (-V + X)$$
$$= +V + X + V - X$$
$$= 2V$$

The interference has been rejected.

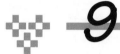

9

Bits and pieces

Not every town has its home studio supplies shop – yet. If you live in London or another major city, then it is well worthwhile having a browse through the high tech department of a good musical instrument shop, where you can see loads of interesting bits and pieces that might earn their keep in a personal recording setup. If you do not live in a studio-aware area, then the catalogues of mail-order suppliers are a must, just to see what is available. Sometimes, you do not realise you have a problem until you see the solution, available for the cost of a telephone call and credit card bill at the end of the month.

Here I present, in no particular order of importance, a modest collection of many of the small items which make my home project studio run more smoothly than it otherwise might. I don't recommend that you go out and buy everything you see here. But every good studio, large or small, will have a fair proportion of these items in regular use. You're bound to see something that takes your eye.

Adaptors

Incompatible connectors are one of the greatest time wasters in any studio operation. Just when you want to do something really adventurous, you find that it involves a mixture of connector types that sends you rushing to the work bench for a soldering iron. The best answer to this problem is to make up short adaptor cables in sufficient quantity to cover any mismatch that may arise. But it is always as well to have a few adaptors such as these to hand. Some, like jack to phono, are not fantastically reliable in use because the weight of the jack plug strains the connection. XLR to XLR sex reversers work well.

Cable

A stock of cable in various types never comes amiss. There is always that extra lead to be made up. I keep three types of cable in my cupboard: lapped screen single for phono leads, foil screen twin for wiring within my racks, and conductive plastic screen twin for XLR and jack leads. If you have more money to spare then you should buy the more expensive type of phono connector which can accept a larger cable diameter and use thicker conductive plastic or lapped screen cable.

Figure 9.1 Lapped screen single, foil screen twin and conductive plastic screen twin cables

Cleaning

Regular cleaning of analogue reel to reel recorders is vital. A clean tape recorder is a happy tape recorder. Isopropyl alcohol is available from chemists. It is a much better head and tape guide cleaner than the alcohol and water mixture sometimes marketed as head cleaner. Your chemist will probably warn you not to drink it as it is definitely not the type of alcohol you would find in a gin and tonic. The pinch roller on any tape recorder gathers a lot of dirt very quickly. Alcohol is usually not so good for shifting this and may damage the rubber. I have always found 'Jif' from the supermarket very efficient, used in minuscule quantities.

You can't clean digital multitracks or DAT recorders in the same way, so you will need to buy cleaning tapes exactly as recommended by the manufacturers. Unfortunately, even these don't clean the recorder thoroughly, and you will have to send the machine for service every so often, depending on how much use it gets. Don't open up a digital recorder and try and clean it yourself, it's a job for an expert.

Apart from analogue and digital recorders, everything else in the studio needs regular cleaning to function at its best. Try and brush dust *away* from the fader slots on the mixing console, and it's a good idea to rotate every control and press every switch once in a while to shift any dirt that might accumulate before it sticks hard and fast.

Figure 9.2 Cleaning and demagnetising

Connectors

The types of connector that you use will be governed mainly by your equipment. Buying the cheapest, especially jacks and phonos, is unwise. They will be difficult to solder and will probably cause trouble in the long term. Studio suppliers usually stock only reliable types. High street electronics hobbyist shops often keep more doubtful brands. Note the difference between the type B jack and the ordinary variety. The type B jack has a smaller tip. Although they are both ¼ inch in diameter, a type B jack should not be plugged into a standard jack socket, and vice versa.

Figure 9.3 Phono, DIN, jack, type B jack, male and female XLR connectors

Editing supplies

If you use a stereo reel-to-reel tape recorder, then you can't manage without this equipment. The photo shows an expensive Editall splicing block, which is extremely good but there are cheaper models available. It is also possible to edit analogue multitrack tapes with a splicing block and splicing tape of the correct size. If you want to edit digital audio, then the equipment necessary could cost up to about a hundred times as much!

Figure 9.4 Editing equipment for reel-to-reel tape

Ironmongery

Blank aluminium panels are used for filling in holes in racks (while you save up for more gear!) and for mounting odd components. In Chapter 4 I showed such a panel in my rack on which I mounted a Quad 306 amplifier. I could also have mounted connectors, controls or switches, as commonly happens in pro studios. The diecast box is also well loved in studios for making up switch or connector boxes etc.

For making holes in metal, the Q-max punch is available from good tool shops. Check the sizes of the panel mounting XLRs you buy and get two punches, one for male and one for female. Of course, you don't have to get into metal bashing if you want to run a home studio – but if you want a more productive studio then it's a great idea to have everything precisely as you want it.

Figure 9.5 Rack strip, diecast box, Q-max punches, blank 19 inch panel, rack bolts, cage nuts and nylon washers

Line up

Analogue reel-to-reel tape recorders do need an occasional line up, to cope with head wear, and to keep up with changing tape formulations. You will need a test tape, which has tones recorded to precise levels, an oscillator, a tweaker (a screwdriver with a very small metal blade which doesn't interfere with the high frequency bias oscillator in the machine), and someone to show you how to do it. Alternatively, there are a number of people who advertise this kind of service.

Pro studios check and line up their machines often, you should have it done at least once a year. Occasionally you may find that your digital

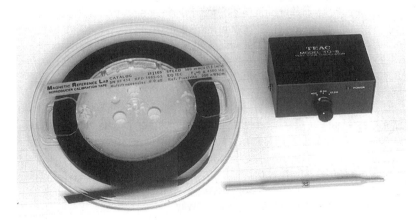

Figure 9.6 Analogue tape recorders need regular line-up

recorder will glitch when playing a tape recorded on someone else's machine. This is a sign that at least one of the two machines needs aligning. This can be done as part of an overall service.

Sticky tape

You will almost certainly find a reel of gaffer tape and a reel of masking tape in any studio. There will always be a time when cables need to be taped down, or something needs holding in place temporarily (cheap studios use gaffer tape to hold their mic stands together!). Masking tape is useful for keeping cables neatly coiled, and also for attaching notes to equipment showing control positions or fader assignments.

Figure 9.7 Gaffer tape and masking tape

Tape supplies

Tape, and associated items, will form most of the running costs of your studio. If you use a DAT machine, buy DAT tapes from studio suppliers rather than the local corner shop. If you have a digital multitrack that runs on video cassettes, make sure you buy exactly the type of cassette recommended by the manufacturer, otherwise you are asking for trouble. The duration of S-VHS cassettes used for ADAT recording is sometimes puzzling. If you buy a tape intended for PAL or SECAM video, then you will get around a quarter of the stated video running time in your ADAT. For example, a nominal 180 minute tape will last just over 40 minutes. In the USA where they have NTSC video, the video tape speed is different, so a 120 minute NTSC video cassette will also last for just over 40 minutes in an ADAT. Other than the amount of tape inside for the stated duration, there is no difference between NTSC and PAL/SECAM video cassettes.

If you use stereo analogue reel-to-reel tape, seven inch spools will be useful, especially if you need to send tapes to other people. The type with the large centre hub is more friendly to tape recorders than the small centre variety. It doesn't hold as much tape of course, but many machines have a tension problem with small hub spools. It is not usually necessary to buy empty 10½ inch spools. As you use up more and more tape, you will probably find yourself giving them away.

Figure 9.8 Analogue tapes, digital tapes and a recordable CD blank

Tools

These items are not compulsory, but any home studio is bound to involve a bit of DIY. I don't need to describe everyday toolkit items which you probably have already – screwdrivers, electric drill etc. Shown here are the items most relevant to the studio. Note especially the side cutters and long-nose pliers. Wire strippers come in an enormous variety. I have found this type, similar to types available from DIY and electrical shops, the most useful for general small quantity work.

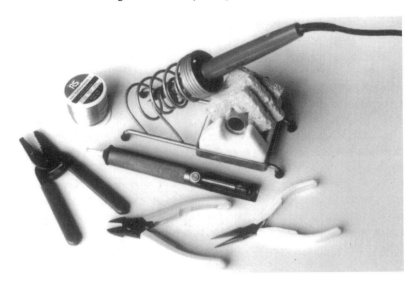

Figure 9.9 Soldering iron, solder, desoldering tool, wire strippers, side cutters and pliers

Wiring

If you get into wiring, then the correct supplies are essential. Bodged wiring will not do. Shown here are binding sleeves, sleeving lubricant, sleeving tool, heat shrink and expanding braid sleeve, heat gun, cable ties and stick on cable tie bases, cable numbers. A hot air paint stripper will work very effectively as a heat gun, a hair dryer isn't hot enough.

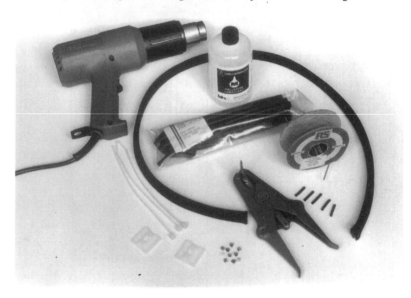

Figure 9.10 Heat gun, expanding braid sleeve, sleeving lubricant, heatshrink sleeve, silicone rubber sleeving, binding sleeves, cable ties, cable tie bases and cable numbers

Miscellaneous

I am sure there could be a thousand and one items under this heading, but here are a few...

Headphones are most essential. There are always times when you want to hear something just that little bit more clearly. They are useful for dealing with noise-conscious neighbours too (you tie them up with the cable!). If you intend to drive foldback headphones for musicians' monitoring from a power amplifier, then you should use high impedance models, preferably all the same type. Make sure that the impedance is 600 ohms or greater.

NAB adaptors are for fitting $10^{1}/_{2}$ inch spools onto stereo tape recorders. The thread adaptor is the bit that goes between the mic clip and the stand. For some unknown reason, mic clips will usually not just screw straight on. Thread adaptors are somehow very easy to lose.

Patchcords are necessary for hooking up equipment via your patchbay. The notebook is for the obvious purpose. You can take too many notes during a session. But when you discover an interesting combination of settings, it is useful to make a quick record.

Spare fuses, of course, are vital. Sooner or later one will expire from old age and if you do not have the right spare to hand, then either the session grinds to a halt or your equipment's safety (yours too) will be compromised by using a fuse of an incorrect rating.

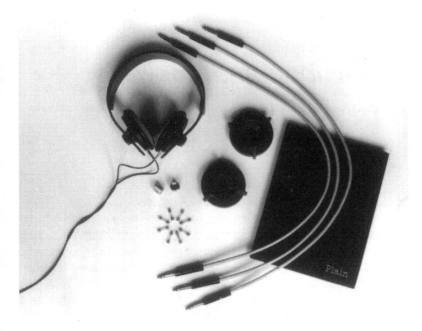

Figure 9.11 Headphones, thread adaptors, fuses, NAB adaptors, patchcords and notebook

Well equipped?

When you have all of these items in your home studio, you can consider yourself well-equipped. Actually, it depends on your particular circumstances what you need, and you might have a use for some things I haven't mentioned. But as far as small items go, the most essential thing to have is a knowledge of where you can get hold of something when the need arises. That and a good idea of what's available.

So, in addition to the bits and pieces shown here, you need catalogues from the studio equipment suppliers for your bookshelf. They make interesting reading, I can tell you (but be advised that some suppliers make a charge for their catalogues). The suppliers I use regularly are Canford Audio, Electromail, Future Film Developments and Studio Spares. From a combination of these four, I find that I can source pretty well everything I need, at the right price (I don't get a discount for plugging their services unfortunately). But I would certainly recommend any home recordist to investigate the other companies. They may have bargains I haven't discovered yet.

10

Questions and answers

If you have read *How to Set Up a Home Recording Studio* right through, then by now you must have formed some ideas on how to go about actually doing it. As I have said from time to time along the way, it's not my intention to present a complete blueprint for a home studio but more to supply a collection of ideas, all of which are relevant and, added together, will supply a large proportion of the necessary information. As I have begun to realise over the years, audio is a very 'bitty' subject. There is no straight-line path from ignorance to complete mastery. Gradually, you pick up more and more information, then suddenly it all gels together and you really do understand what's going on.

At this stage in *How to Set Up a Home Recording Studio* it is time to reflect on the process of assembling a studio system. To go back and examine the key facts so that knowledge gained will hopefully be knowledge retained. Here are some of the questions I have been asked by home and project studio enthusiasts. I hope the answers shed more light on the subject for you.

Anyone can make a good recording – if they have lots of expensive equipment. Right?

Not necessarily. Professional equipment is designed so it is as easy as possible to get good results – but at a price. Equipment suitable for home and project studios often has as many facilities, but the overall performance may be compromised. Yes, you will be more likely to get good recordings with the really expensive gear, but in your home studio you have time to experiment and, with care and a bit of ingenuity, impressive results are possible.

What musical instruments do I need in my home studio?

As far as keyboards go, you need at least one sampler and one synth. The sampler can access a tremendous range of sounds, the synth is capable of subtle variations in the tones it can produce. The two complement each other very well. It won't hurt you to play an acoustic instrument either, or find someone who can!

Can I get everything I need from my local music shop?

You can probably get most of the equipment, but bear in mind that the staff of music shops often know a lot about the equipment but not so much about the real process of recording. There are a number of mail order professional studio suppliers who concentrate on recording equipment and the bits and bobs you need to make it all fit together properly.

How many tape tracks do I need?

At least eight. The sound quality of four track recorders can be amazingly good, but for modern musical styles having just four tracks can be very restricting, unless you use your four tracker in conjunction with a sizable MIDI system. Even with eight tracks, you have to plan your recordings carefully. With 16 or more tracks, you have room to be more spontaneous and creative. When you have 24 audio tracks at your disposal, your project studio has, at least in this respect, reached a professional level.

I have a lot of MIDI gear. I don't think I would benefit from having a multitrack tape recorder as well.

You would, because as long as you have a tape/MIDI synchroniser you can use any combination of your MIDI equipment on any track of the tape. This vastly increases the range of sounds and effects you can obtain. Tape is also a safer storage medium. Whatever you put on tape today will be there tomorrow. With synth and MIDI data stored on a computer disk, it's easy to make a mistake and lose something important.

How many channels should the mixer have?

You can probably work it out yourself, but a good rule of thumb to start with is at least one and a half times as many channels as tape tracks (or tape tracks plus MIDI instrument outputs). As you add to your effects rack you will undoubtedly find that your requirement for more channels grows, so it pays to think ahead.

What type of recorder should I have for mastering?

DAT or reel-to-reel. The quality of ordinary cassettes, even chrome or metal, is just not good enough for music mastering. A reel-to-reel recorder should be half-track stereo (definitely not quarter track – examples still crop up on the secondhand market) and must run at a speed of 15 inches per second. It is an advantage if it takes large 10^1/$_2$ inch NAB spools. The advantage of DAT is that it is pretty much a music industry standard and offers a very clear sound. Reel-to-reel can be edited with inexpensive tools and has a warm sound quality that many engineers like.

Should I use any special type of tape?

Yes, a well known brand of DAT tape from a studio supplier. When you have found a brand that you like, stick to it. Reel-to-reel owners should always use the brand for which the recorder was lined up. If in doubt, ask the supplier who you bought the machine from, they should know. Ampex 456 is the most common brand. Some other brands are compatible with 456 and you may use them without realignment. Ampex 499 is also compatible with 456 but realignment is necessary to get the absolute best out of this tape.

Do I need dynamic or capacitor microphones?

The minimum requirement is for a dynamic mic with a good high frequency response, such as a Beyerdynamic M201. Some types, like the Shure SM58, are good mics, but lack top end response making them dull on metallic percussion instruments. Small diaphragm capacitor mics usually sound very clear but can the lack 'presence' and 'body' of more expensive large diaphragm mics. Aim to collect a variety of different types of microphone as your studio grows.

What about signal processing?

A good reverb is essential. Multieffects units are useful in addition to a dedicated reverb, but they can be fiddly to program and operate. Effects units that only do one job usually do it well and can be much more straightforward to use.

Do I need big monitoring speakers?

Big speakers can produce a very satisfying sound but the professionals have shown that it is possible to get a good mix on small near field monitors, even if you have to imagine some of the bass! There are plenty of specialised studio monitors available at reasonable prices so you should steer clear of cheap hifi speakers. If you can afford near field monitors and good quality main monitors, then it's nice to have the option to switch between the two pairs.

Are good cables important?

Yes. Buy your cables from a studio supplier rather than from a hifi shop. The cables in hifi shops are usually either absolute rubbish, or they are so exotic that you will spend a disproportionate amount of your budget on them. With semi-pro gear, keep the cable lengths as short as possible.

What causes hum?

Usually an earth loop where there is a complete electric circuit connected through the mains earth, as described in Chapter 5. If you are getting a hum, completely disconnect everything but the mixing console, power amplifier and speakers. If you still have a hum, then check that the mixer and amp are both connected to mains earth. If they are, snip the screen wire in the connectors at the inputs to the amp, making sure that no strands of wire are loose within the connector. The hum should now disappear. Reconnect the equipment piece by piece, and whenever the hum reappears, snip the screen connections to the new equipment.

Should I buy ready-made cables or make them up myself?

If you are good at soldering (and anyone can be with practice), it is better and cheaper to make cables yourself. If not, buy them from a studio supplier.

Do I need a patchbay?

Definitely. You can get by using point-to-point wiring for so long, but your studio will be more efficient if all your equipment is wired to a patchbay.

Is it possible to mount equipment in a rack even if it has no rack-mount ears?

Very often it is possible to mount equipment on a blank 19 inch rack panel, with just a little metalwork. Alternatively, some of the studio suppliers sell rack mount equipment – shelves, brackets etc. It's much more tidy to have your equipment in a rack. Bear in mind that if you alter the equipment itself, you will invalidate the guarantee.

I can't afford the latest gear, only second-hand stuff. Does that mean my recordings are going to be rubbish?

Not necessarily, but make sure that you give the equipment a thorough test before you buy, and ask to see the owner's original receipt or you may be buying stolen goods which will be taken from you when the police catch up with them. Secondhand reel-to-reel tape recorders can be a particular source of trouble. Test every track, and check the amount of head wear. The wider the flat patch on the head, the sooner it will be time for an expensive replacement. Tape handling must be smooth. Secondhand DAT machines are best avoided since they are full of high precision components. A DAT machine may be able to record and play back perfectly, but its tapes may be unplayable on any other machine. If you are buying a secondhand mixer, test every channel. Check knobs and faders for 'scratchiness'. If you are buying a synth, test every note and every knob, control and switch.

I'm going to have my home studio in my bedroom, is that a good place for it?

No! And tell your parents that I said so, if they are trying to put a block on your ambitions! If you think about how much you have paid for all the gear, then it obviously deserves a dedicated home all of its own. Four places that spring to mind are the basement, loft, garage or spare room (not the cupboard under the stairs – although I have seen some outside broadcast vans that had smaller sound control rooms!). If the room you choose is subject to damp, as basements often are, then you will need to take steps to ensure that the equipment doesn't suffer.

I'm trying to economise on the acoustic treatment. After all, it's the equipment that is most important.

Yes, the basic equipment is most important, but after that it is what you hear that will affect the quality of your recordings most, and that is governed by the acoustics of your studio. If you were thinking of buying an extra synth for a few hundred pounds, it might be better to think of spending that money on some basic acoustic treatment.

I want to soundproof my studio. Do I need a lot of foam and egg boxes?

Soft materials will help reduce the sound levels inside the studio. They will absorb a large proportion of reverberant sound that is mostly unwanted anyway. Apart from that, they won't stop much sound getting out. If a piece of foam absorbs 75% of the sound that hits it, that is only the same as a 12dB reduction. Sound insulation, rather than absorption, is governed by the mass of a partition and whether it is well sealed or has any gaps around the edges. Covering the walls of a studio with cardboard egg boxes is an old myth that never seems to go away. The right type of egg boxes will provide good acoustic treatment (not insulation), but only at high frequencies. You must consider all the frequencies in the audio range.

Does modern equipment require a lot of maintenance?

Reel-to-reel tape recorders need regular cleaning – the heads, guides and rollers. Other equipment seems remarkably maintenance-free, apart from digital recorders which need to be serviced every so often. If things do go wrong, don't take your precious recording equipment to your local Mr Fixit – he may be reasonably good with common or garden TVs and videos, but a dodgy digital effects unit might be outside his experience. If in doubt, contact the manufacturer or distributor. They should have their own service department, or they will be able to recommend someone competent.

That hopefully covers most of the questions that arise immediately. But are you still asking yourself 'Should I go ahead and do it?'. Well of course you should! It's a great way to have fun. But a home studio is not simply a collection of fancy equipment. It is the fashioning of that equipment into a tool for creating music. And it is a tool that will work best when you design it according to your needs. You are bound to come up problems along the way, perhaps problems that have not been covered in this book. But your solutions will go towards making your studio unique and totally unlike anyone else's. From that uniqueness, hopefully, you will find your own individual style of recording.

I wish you luck with your home project studio, and as much pleasure from your home recording as I get from mine.

11

Glossary

Acoustics   More properly called 'room acoustics'. The interaction between sound and the surfaces in a room or auditorium.

Acoustic treatment   Measures taken to improve the subjective sound quality of a room.

Adaptor   A short cable or connector which allows two normally incompatible connectors to be mated.

Auxiliary return   A mixing console input similar to a channel but with reduced facilities, usually just level and pan. Often used for reverb and other effects units.

Auxiliary send   Besides the normal group outputs routed to the multitrack tape recorder, mixing consoles have Auxiliary Sends to route signal to foldback and effects units.

Balanced connection   A method of connection which uses two signal conductors plus a screen to cancel out interference picked up in the cable. Professional equipment and an increasing amount of semi-pro equipment is balanced. Domestic hifi is unbalanced.

Bantam jack   A small version of the Type B jack connector.

BNC   A type of video connector.

Braided screen   Woven copper wire which surrounds the signal conductors in a cable and is connected to earth. Prevents interference getting into the signal conductors.

Bucket   Properly called 'solder bucket'. The point at which a cable conductor is soldered to an XLR connector.

Cage nut   Square nut with a springy metal surround used in 19 inch equipment racks.

Capacitance   Electrical phenomenon where a high frequency signal passes between two conductors even when there is no direct connection.

Capacitor microphone   A high quality microphone which exploits the capacitance effect and needs to be powered.

Cassette recorder   Domestic cassette machine, not to be confused with a DAT or reel-to-reel tape recorder.

Channel   One input section of a mixing console. Typical consoles suitable for the home or project studio have between 16 and 32 channels.

Chinagraph   Brand name of a wax pencil used for marking tape for editing.

Commercial studio   A studio available for hire.

Compressor Device used to reduce the difference between high and low level signals.

DAT Digital audio tape. The professional standard for stereo music mastering.

Demo A recording made to play to a publisher or record company, not for commercial release.

Desoldering tool Tool to remove solder from a connection. Sometimes called a 'solder sucker'.

Diecast box Aluminium alloy box used for mounting switches and connectors.

Digital delay Device used to produce single and multiple echoes.

Dry joint A solder joint which is not air-tight.

Dynamic microphone A type of microphone which does not need powering, but typically does not sound as clear as a capacitor microphone.

Earth loop When there is more than one connection to mains earth in a system, a low pitched hum will be heard through the speakers.

Earth The planet we live on. Electrical systems use the Earth as a zero voltage reference and a rubbish bin for unwanted currents.

Editing block Metal block used to align reel-to-reel tape ready for joining. Not available for digital cassette recording formats.

Effects Devices connected to the mixing console to enhance a sound.

Electronic balancing System of making a balanced connection in equipment which does not use transformers.

EQ Equalisation. Each channel of the mixing console will have an EQ section which is used to balance the levels of high, middle and low frequencies.

Flux Substance which helps solder flow when molten.

Foil screen Aluminium foil wound round the signal conductors in a cable and connected to earth. Prevents interference getting into the signal conductors.

Foldback Headphone monitoring for musicians in the studio.

FX Abbreviation for 'effects'.

Gaffer tape Strong cloth sticky tape often used by sound engineers.

GPO jack Old name for type B jack connector.

Half track stereo The normal stereo reel-to-reel tape recorder which records two channels of audio across practically the full width of the tape.

Heat gun Like a hair dryer but hotter. Used to grip heat-shrink sleeving onto a cable or loom.

Home studio Studio set up for the benefit of an individual. Not normally available for hire.

Hum Low pitched buzz. A common form of electrical interference usually caused by an earth loop.

IEC A European body which sets standards on various things such as tape recorder equalisation and mains connectors.

Interference Unwanted electrical signals contaminating the sound signal.

IPS Abbreviation for inches per second.

Isopropyl alcohol Type of alcohol used for cleaning reel-to-reel tape recorder heads.

Jackfield UK English for 'patchbay'.

Jack connector (type A) Connector often used by musicians, and frequently found in home and project studios. Professionals prefer XLRs.

Lapped screen Strands of copper wire wound round the signal conductors in a cable and connected to earth. They prevent interference getting into the signal conductors.

Level The loudness of an acoustic or electrical signal.

Loom A number of individual cables gathered together.

Master

1 The stereo tape recorder.

2 The output section of a mixing console which is connected to the stereo tape recorder.

3 The finished recording.

MIDI Musical Instrument Digital Interface. Used for connecting synthesisers, samplers, expanders and keyboards etc together.

Mixing console The nerve centre of the recording studio where all the signals come together and are blended to taste.

Module A rack mounting unit which has the sound producing capabilities of a synthesiser but is driven by MIDI rather than a keyboard. Sometimes known as a synthesiser module or MIDI module.

Monitor

1 Short for 'monitor loudspeaker'.

2 To listen closely to the loudspeakers.

3 Mixing console input for listening to the output of the multitrack tape recorder while overdubbing.

Multieffects unit Device capable of several different types of effect.

Multicore cable Cable which carries several separate audio signals.

Multicore solder Solder wire which contains cores of flux.

Multitrack Short for 'multitrack tape recorder'. A tape recorder which can record several different musical lines on separate tracks the tape.

NAB spool 10¹/₂ inch spool with a large centre hole.

NAB An American body which sets standards on various things such as tape recorder equalisation and tape spools.

Noise gate Device used for cutting out background noise when an instrument is not playing.

Normalling Patchbay wiring technique which reduces the need for patchcords in a normal recording situation.

Outboard Effects units.

Pan A mixing console control which changes the apparent position of a signal between the stereo speakers.

Patchbay US English for 'jackfield'. A unit with many type B jack sockets which are connected to virtually all the inputs and outputs of the equipment in the studio. Saves searching round the back of the equipment for the connectors.

Patchcords Short cables used for connecting equipment via the patchbay.

PA Abbreviation for 'public address'.

Phono connector Difficult to use and often unreliable connector found in home and project studio recording equipment. Professionals prefer jacks and XLRs.

Plasterboard Material commonly used for sound insulation.

Portastudio A multitrack cassette recorder with integral mixer. A trade name of Tascam.

Power amplifier An amplifier without controls, other than level, that drives the monitor speakers.

Q-Max punch Sheet metal punch, available in various sizes.

Quarter track stereo A system of stereo tape recording which records two tracks on half the width of the tape. Totally unsuitable for the home studio.

Rack strip Used in 19 inch rack construction. Punched with square holes suitable for mounting cage nuts.

Rack Virtually all studio equipment, unless it is designed to be free standing, has standard fixings for mounting in a 19 inch rack.

Reel-to-reel Tape recorder suitable for studio use. Not to be confused with the domestic cassette recorder.

Reverb Device which simulates the natural echoes in a room.

Rockwool A mineral wool substance which is commonly used for acoustic treatment.

Sampler Device which can record sound digitally and play it back at different pitches, controlled by a MIDI keyboard.

Screen Found in audio cables, prevents interference getting to the signal conductors.

Sequencer Device for recording and manipulating MIDI data, such as that produced by a MIDI keyboard. May be a dedicated unit but is usually supplied as computer software.

Sleeve Various types of rubber and plastic sleeves are available for covering bare conductors and for making cable looms.

Sleeving tool Device for placing sleeving on a cable.

Solder sucker Alternative term for 'desoldering tool'.

Splicing tape Special sticky tape used for joining tape in editing.

Synchronisation Linking together a MIDI sequencer and multitrack record, multitrack and video, or two or more audio recorders.

Synthesiser Musical instrument which generates sound from electronic or digital circuits.

Track On a multitrack tape recorder, each track carries a separate musical part.

Transformer A device which consists of coils of wire wound round a metal core. Used in balanced equipment. Imitated by 'electronic balancing' circuits.

Tweaker Colloquial term for a screwdriver with a very small metal blade used for tape recorder alignment.

Type A jack The standard $1/4$ inch jack connector.

Type B jack Type of connector used in patchbays. Also known as GPO jack or type 316.

U The unit of vertical 19 inch rack space. $1U = 1^{3}/_{4}$ inches.

XLR connector The standard professional audio connector.

12

Directory of manufacturers and suppliers

Computers
TSC (Macintosh), 9 Hatton Street, London NW8 8PR, Tel 0171 258 3454

Effects units
Arbiter Group plc (Digitech), Wilberforce Road, London NW9 6AX, Tel 0181 202 1199
Drawmer, Charlotte Street Business Centre, Charlotte Street, Wakefield, West Yorkshire, WF1 1UH, Tel 01924 378669
Klark Teknik plc, Klark Industrial Park, Walter Nash Road, Kidderminster, Worcs DY11 7HJ, Tel 01562 741515
Peavey Electronics, Hatton House, Hunters Road, Weldon Industrial Estate, Corby, Northants, NN17 5JE, Tel 01536 205520
Sound Technology (Alesis), Letchworth Point, Letchworth, Hertfordshire SG6 1ND, Tel 01462 480000
TSC (Zoom), 9 Hatton Street, London NW8 8PR, Tel 0171 258 3454
Yamaha Kemble Music, Sherbourne Drive, Tilbrook, Milton Keynes MK7 8BL, Tel 01908 366700

Hard disk recorders
Akai UK, Haslemere Heathrow Estate, Parkway, Hounslow, Middlesex TW4 6NQ, Tel 0181 897 6388
Digidesign, Avid Technology Ltd.,Westside Complex, Pinewood Studios, Iver Heath, Pinewood, Bucks SL0 0NH, Tel 01753 653322
Micropolis, 4 Worton Drive, Worton Grange, Reading, Berkshire RG2 0DW, Tel 01734 751315
Roland UK, Atlantic Close, Swansea Enterprise Park, Swansea, West Glamorgan SA7 9FJ, Tel 01792 700139
Soundscape Digital, Crichton House, Mount Stuart Square, Cardiff Bay, Cardiff CF1 6DR, Tel 01222 450120
Studio Audio & Video Ltd (Sadie), The Old School, Stretham, Ely, Cambridge CB6 3LD, Tel 01353 648888
Vestax Europe Ltd, 18 St Christopher's Road, Haslemere, Surrey GU27 1DQ, Tel 01428 653117

Headphones
AKG UK, Harman Audio, Unit 2, Borehamwood Industrial Park, Rowley

Lane, Borehamwood, Herts, Tel 0181 207 5050

Audio Technica, Technica House, Royal London Industrial Estate, Old Lane, Leeds LS11 8AG, Tel 0113 227 1441

Beyerdynamic, Unit 14, Cliffe Industrial Estate, Lewes, Sussex BN8 6JL, Tel 01273 479411

Peavey Electronics, Hatton House, Hunters Road, Weldon Industrial Estate, Corby, Northants NN17 5JE, Tel 01536 205520

Sennheiser UK (Sennheiser & Neumann), 12 Davies Way, Knaves Beech Business Centre, Loudwater, High Wycombe, Bucks HP10 9QY, Tel 01628 524900

Magazines

Sound on Sound, Media House, Burrel Road, St Ives, Cambs PE17 4LE, Tel 01480 461244

Audio Media, AM Publishing Ltd, Atlantica House, 11 Station Road, St Ives, Cambs PE17 4BH, Tel 01480 461555

Future Music, Future Publishing, 30 Monmouth Street, Bath BA1 2BW, Tel 01225 442244

The Mix, MMP Music Ltd, Alexander House, Forehill, Ely, Cambs CB7 4AF, Tel 01353 665577

Pro Sound News, Miller Freeman Entertainment, 8th Floor, Ludgate House, 245 Blackfriars Road, London SE1 9UR, Tel 0171 620 3636

Studio Sound, Miller Freeman Entertainment, 8th Floor, Ludgate House, 245 Blackfriars Road, London SE1 9UR, Tel 0171 620 3636

Microphones

AKG UK, Harman Audio, Unit 2, Borehamwood Industrial Park, Rowley Lane, Borehamwood, Herts, Tel 0181 207 5050

Audio Technica, Technica House, Royal London Industrial Estate, Old Lane, Leeds LS11 8AG, Tel 0113 227 1441

Beyerdynamic, Unit 14, Cliffe Industrial Estate, Lewes, Sussex BN8 6JL, Tel 01273 479411

HW International (Shure), 161-171 Willoughby Lane, London N17 0SB, Tel 0181 808 2222

Sennheiser UK (Sennheiser & Neumann), 12 Davies Way, Knaves Beech Business Centre, Loudwater, High Wycome, Bucks HP10 9QY, Tel 01628 524900

Spirit by Soundcraft, Harman International Industries Ltd, Cranbourne House, Cranbourne Industrial Estate, Cranbourne Road, Potters Bar, Herts EN6 3JN, Tel 01707 665000

Mixing consoles

Allen & Heath Ltd, Kernick Industrial Estate, Penryn, Falmouth, Cornwall TR10 9LU, Tel 01326 372070

Amek Systems & Controls Ltd, New Islington Mill, Regent Trading Estate, Oldfield Road, Salford M5 4SX, Tel 0161 834 6747

Behringher UK, St Vincent House, 59 Woodbridge Road, Guildford, Surrey GU1 4RF, Tel 01483 458877

DDA, Unit 1, Inwood Business Park, Whitton Road, Hounslow, Middlesex TW3 2EB, Tel 0181 570 7161

Key Audio Systems (Mackie), Unit D37, Robjohns Road, Chelmsford, Essex CM1 3AG, Tel 01245 344001

Malcolm Toft Associates, 27 Ash Hill Road, Ash, Hampshire GU12 6AD, Tel 01252 318700

Soundcraft, Harman International Industries Ltd, Cranbourne House, Cranbourne Industrial Estate, Cranbourne Road, Potters Bar, Herts EN6 3JN, Tel 01707 665000

Soundtracs plc, Unit 21-D, Blenheim Road, Longmead Industrial Estate, Epsom, Surrey KT19 9XN, Tel 0181 388 5000

Spirit by Soundcraft, Harman International Industries Ltd, Cranbourne House, Cranbourne Industrial Estate, Cranbourne Road, Potters Bar, Herts EN6 3JN, Tel 01707 665000

Studiomaster, Studiomaster House, Chaul End Lane, Luton, Beds LU4 8EZ, Tel 01582 570370

Tascam UK, 5 Marlin House, The Croxley Centre, Watford, Herts WD1 8YA, Tel 01923 819630

Yamaha Kemble Music, Sherbourne Drive, Tilbrook, Milton Keynes MK7 8BL, Tel 01908 366700

Patchbays

Connectronics, 9 Haslemere Industrial Estate, Bishops Stortford CM23 3HQ, Tel 01279 506684

Isotrack, PO Box 747, Poole, Dorset BH12 4YG, Tel 01202 747191

Kelsey Acoustics, 27 Beethoven Street, London W10 4LL, Tel 0181 964 8000

Plasmec Systems Ltd, Farnham Business Park, Weydon Lane, Farnham GU9 8QL, Tel 01252 721236

Power amplifiers

Bryston, Unit 4, Melinite Industrial Estate, Brixton Road, Watford, Herts WD2 5SL, Tel 01923 249119

Chevin Research, Otley Mills, Otley LS21 3JP, Tel 01943 466060

Citronic Pro Audio Ltd, Halifax Road, Bowerhill, Melksham, Wilts SN12 6UB, Tel 01225 705600

Crest Audio, 5a Wilbury Grove, Hove, BN3 3JQ, Tel 01273 693513

Malcolm Hill Associates, Hollingbourne House, Hollingbourne, Kent ME17 1QJ, Tel 01622 880601

Quad Electroacoustics Ltd, Huntingdon, Cambs PE18 7DB, Tel 01480 52561

Sound Technology (Alesis), Letchworth Point, Letchworth, Hertfordshire SG6 1ND, Tel 01462 480000

Yamaha Kemble Music, Sherbourne Drive, Tilbrook, Milton Keynes MK7 8BL, Tel 01908 366700

Power distribution

EMO Systems Ltd, Durham Road, Urshaw Moor, Durham City DH7 7LF, Tel 0191 373 0787

Samplers
Akai UK, Haslemere Heathrow Estate, Parkway, Hounslow, Middlesex TW4 6NQ, Tel 0181 897 6388

Emu Systems, Suite 6, Adam Ferguson House, Eskmills Industrial Park, Musselburgh, EH21 7PG, Tel 0131 653 6556

Roland UK, Atlantic Close, Swansea Enterprise Park, Swansea, West Glamorgan SA7 9FJ, Tel 01792 700139

Sequencers
Harman Audio (Steinberg), Unit 2, Borehamwood Industrial Park, Rowley Lane, Borehamwood, Herts WD6 5PZ, Tel 0181 207 5050

MusicTrack (Mark of the Unicorn), PO Box 4, Arlesey, Bedfordshire SG15 6AA, Tel 01462 733310

Sound Technology (Emagic), Letchworth Point, Letchworth, Herfordshire SG6 1ND, Tel 01462 480000

TSC (Opcode), 9 Hatton Street, London NW8 8PR, Tel 0171 258 3454

Speakers
ATC Loudspeaker Technology Ltd, Gypsy Lane, Aston Down, Stroud GL6 8HR, Tel 01285 760561

B&W Loudspeakers Ltd, Meadow Road, Worthing BN11 2RX, Tel 01903 820415

Celestion International Ltd, Foxhall Road, Ipswich, IP3 8JP, Tel 01473 322222

Harman Audio (JBL), Unit 2, Borehamwood Industrial Park, Rowley Lane, Borehamwood, Herts WD6 5PZ, Tel 0181 207 5050

KEF Audio UK Ltd, Eccleston Road, Tovil, Maidstone, Kent ME15 6QP, Tel 01622 672261

Shuttlesound (Electrovoice), 4 The Willows Centre, Willow Lane, Mitcham, Surrey, CR4 4NX, Tel 0181 646 7114

Soundcraft, Harman International Industries Ltd, Cranbourne House, Cranbourne Industrial Estate, Cranbourne Road, Potters Bar, Herts EN6 3JN, Tel 01707 665000

Sound Technology (Alesis), Letchworth Point, Letchworth, Hertfordshire SG6 1ND, Tel 01462 480000

Spendor Audio Systems Ltd, 47 Station Road Industrial Estate, Hailsham BN27 2ER, Tel 01323 843474

Yamaha Kemble Music, Sherbourne Drive, Tilbrook, Milton Keynes MK7 8BL, Tel 01908 366700

Studio design
Munro Associates, Unit 21, Riverside Workshops, 28 Park Street, London SE1 9EQ, Tel 0171 403 3808

Nick Whitaker Electroacoustics, 21-23 Greenwich Market, London SE10 9HZ, Tel 0181 853 2865

Recording Architecture Ltd, 21-23 Greenwich Market, London SE10 9HZ, Tel 0181 858 6883

Studio suppliers

Canford Audio plc, Crowther Road, Washington, Tyne & Wear NE38 0BW, Tel 0191 417 0057

Future Film Developments, Network House, 64 Oxford Road, New Denham, UxbridgeUB9 4DN, Tel 01895 813730

Raper and Wayman Ltd, Unit 3, Crusader Estate, 167 Hermitage Road, London N4 1LZ, Tel 0181 800 8288

Studio Spares, 61/63 Rochester Place, London NW1 9JU, Tel 0171 485 4908

Turnkey Studio Systems, 14 Flitcroft Street, London WC2H 0DT, Tel 0171 240 4036

Synthesisers

Korg UK Ltd, 8-9 The Crystal Centre, Elmgrove Road, Harrow HA1 2YR, Tel 0181 427 5377

Roland UK, Atlantic Close, Swansea Enterprise Park, Swansea, West Glamorgan SA7 9FJ, Tel 01792 700139

Technics Musical Instruments, Willoughby Road, Bracknell, Berkshire RG12 8FP, Tel 01344 853153

TSC, 9 Hatton Street, London NW8 8PR, Tel 0171 258 3454

Yamaha Kemble Music, Sherbourne Drive, Tilbrook, Milton Keynes MK7 8BL, Tel 01908 366700

Tape recorders (analogue and digital)

Graff Electronic Machines Ltd., Woodhill Road, Collingham, Newark, Notts NG23 7NR, Tel 01636 893036

HHB Communications Ltd, 73-75 Scrubs Lane, London NW10 6QU, Tel 0181 962 5000

Panasonic Professional Audio, Willoughby Road, Bracknell, Berks RG12 8FP, Tel 01344 853152

SCV London (Fostex), 6-24 Southgate Road, London N1 3JJ, Tel 0171 923 1892

Sound Technology (Alesis), Letchworth Point, Letchworth, Hertfordshire SG6 1ND, Tel 01462 480000

Tascam UK, 5 Marlin House, The Croxley Centre, Watford, Herts WD1 8YA, Tel 01923 819630

Index